THE OTHER SONG BOOK

The Fellowship Publications
Phoenix, AZ 85076

ISBN 0-89066-060-3

The Other Songbook, © 1984, 1987 by Dave Anderson.
The Fellowship Publications, P.O. Box 51510, Phoenix, AZ 85076

Printed in the United States of America.

Welcome to THE OTHER SONGBOOK — to songs of praise and truth about God's love and faithfulness.

You will find classic hymns of faith, old gospel favorites, children's songs (some of which you probably haven't sung for years), and many new songs of praise and worship. . . all right here!

Every Christian knows that the expression of praise through music and singing is special to God. The musician is one of the first occupations mentioned in Scripture (Genesis 4:21). Did you know God created us with a greater capacity to feel and think and remember when music is involved? It's true. And my prayer is that Christians all over the world will use more music to remember God's promises.

"Rev. Dick Hamlin has said:

"Music prepares the heart for worship and commitment. Music is the greatest mood alternator of all, and unlocks the ministry of God in the untrespassed soil of a person's soul. People love singing. They love being moved even when there is not a song in their hearts."

You will enjoy this book. Begin by singing through the books of the Old and New Testaments — memorize both songs and you can start humming when someone tells you to turn to Ezekiel.

Sing your way along a 500-year-old path of wonderful, simple, profound Christian songs. Let God touch your soul and mind, ministering His joy and comfort to you as you sing one song after another.

Truth must be sung!

Why the unique name? Your church already has an "official" book of songs. This is THE OTHER SONGBOOK!

HOW MAJESTIC IS YOUR NAME 1

Michael W. Smith
Arr. by Henry Wiens

2 A MIGHTY FORTRESS

Martin Luther
Tr., Frederick Henry Hedge

Martin Luther
Arr., Traditional

1. A might - y for - tress is ___ our God,
2. Did we in our ___ own strength con - fide,
3. And though this world, with dev - ils filled,
4. That word a - bove all earth - ly pow'rs,

A
Our
Should
No

bul - wark nev - er fail - ing:
striv - ing would be los - ing:
threat - en to un - do ___ us:
thanks to them, a - bid - eth:

Our
Were
We
The

help - er he ___ a - mid ___ the flood
not the right Man on ___ our side,
will not fear, for God ___ hath willed
Spir - it and ___ the gifts ___ are ours

Of
The
His
Through

3 ALL DAY SONG

Words and Music by
John Fischer

1. Love Him in the morn-in' when you see the sun a-ris-in',
2. And in the in-be-tween time when you feel the pres-sure com-in',

Love Him in the eve-nin' 'cause He took you through the day; —
Re-mem-ber that He loves you and He prom-is-es to stay. —

Fine

When you think you got to wor-ry ___ 'cause it

seems the thing to do; Re-mem-ber He ain't in a hur-

ry. He's al-ways got time for you.

D.C. al Fine

ALL HAIL THE POWER

Oliver Holden
Arr., Roger Nachtway

5

ALL THY WORKS
SHALL PRAISE THEE

Ps. 145: 10-13
Adapted by D. G.

Dale Garratt

king - dom is an ev - er - last - ing king - dom; Thy do -

min - ion en - dur - eth through - out all gen - er - a - tions.

ALLELUIA 6

Jerry Sinclair
Dino Prod.

With quiet adoration

1. Al - le - lu - ia, _____ Al - le - lu - ia, _____ Al - le -

lu - ia, _____ Al - le - lu - ia, _____ Al - le - lu - ia.

2. How I love him   3. Blessed Jesus   4. My Redeemer   5. Jesus is Lord   6. Alleluia

7
BE STILL, MY SOUL

Katharina von Schlegel
Tr. by Jane L. Borthwick

Jean Sibelius

1. Be still, my soul: the Lord is on thy side; _____ Bear pa-tient-
2. Be still, my soul: thy God doth un-der-take _____ To guide the
3. Be still, my soul: the hour is has-tening on _____ When we shall

ly the cross of grief or pain; _____ Leave to thy God to
fu-ture as He has the past. _____ Thy hope, thy con-fi-
be for-ev-er with the Lord, _____ When dis-ap-point-ment,

or-der and pro-vide; _____ In ev-ery change He
dence let noth-ing shake; _____ All now mys-te-rious
grief, and fear are gone, _____ Sor-row for-got, love's

faith-ful will re-main. _____ Be still, my soul: thy
shall be bright at last. _____ Be still, my soul: the
pur-est joys re-stored. _____ Be still, my soul: when

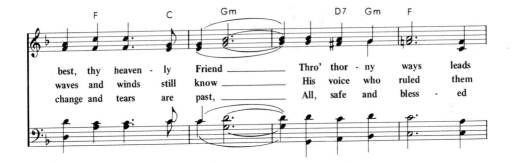

best, thy heaven - ly Friend _____ Thro' thor - ny ways leads
waves and winds still know _____ His voice who ruled them
change and tears are past, _____ All, safe and bless - ed

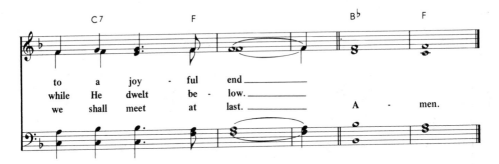

to a joy - ful end _____
while He dwelt be - low. _____
we shall meet at last. _____ A - men.

LORD, LAY SOME SOUL UPON MY HEART 8

Dr. Leon Tucker

David H. Johnson

Lord, lay some soul up - on my heart, And love that soul thru me; _____

And may I hum - bly do my part To win that soul for Thee. _____

9 BEAUTIFUL SAVIOR

Munster Gesangbuch
Tr. Joseph A. Seiss

Silesian Folk-Tune
Hoffmann von Fallersleben's Volkslieder

1. Beau - ti - ful Sav - ior! King of cre - a - tion!
2. Fair are the mead - ows, Fair - er the wood - lands,
3. Fair is the sun - shine, Fair - er the moon - light
4. Beau - ti - ful Sav - ior! Lord of the na - tions!

Son of God and Son of Man!
Robed in flow'rs of bloom - ing spring;
And the spark - ling stars on high;
Son of God and Son of Man!

Tru - ly I'd love Thee, Tru - ly I'd serve Thee,
Je - sus is fair - er; Je - sus is pur - er;
Je - sus shines bright - er, Je - sus shines pur - er;
Glo - ry and hon - or, Praise, a - dor - a - tion,

Light of my soul, my joy, my crown!
He makes our sorrow - ing spir - it sing.
Than all the an - gels in the sky.
Now and for - ev - er - more be Thine!

BEHOLD WHAT MANNER OF LOVE

Words and Music by
Patricia Van Tine

Be - hold what man - ner of love the Fa - ther has giv - en un - to us! Be - hold what man - ner of love the Fa - ther has giv - en un - to us! That we should be called the chil - dren of God, That we should be called the chil - dren of God.

11 BECAUSE HE LIVES

W. J. and Gloria Gaither

William J. Gaither

1. God sent His Son, they called Him Je - sus;
2. How sweet to hold a new - born ba - by
3. And then one day I'll cross the riv - er;

He came to love, heal, and for - give.
And feel the pride and joy He gives;
I'll fight life's fi nal war with pain.

He lived and died to buy my par - don;
But great - er still the calm as - sur - ance
And then as death gives way to vic - tory,

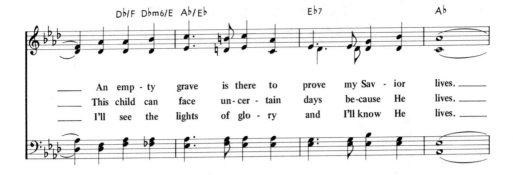

An emp-ty grave is there to prove my Sav-ior lives. ___
This child can face un-cer-tain days be-cause He lives. ___
I'll see the lights of glo-ry and I'll know He lives. ___

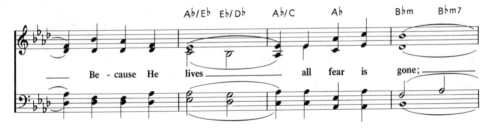

Be - cause He lives ___ I can face to - mor - row; ___

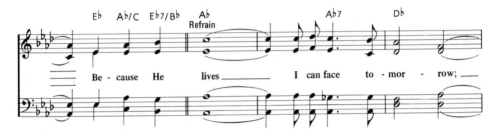

Be - cause He lives ___ all fear is gone; ___

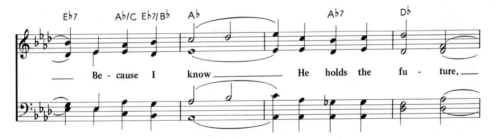

Be - cause I know ___ He holds the fu - ture, ___

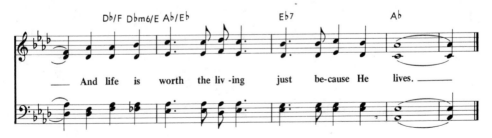

And life is worth the liv -ing just be-cause He lives. ___

12 BELOVED, LET US LOVE ONE ANOTHER

I John 4: 7,8

Dennis Ryder

Beloved, — let us — love — one another. —

For love is of God, — and everyone that loveth — is born of God — and knoweth — God, — He that loveth — not, — knoweth not God, — for God is love. — Beloved, — let us — love — one another. —

BLESS HIS HOLY NAME

13

Ps. 103: 1-2

Andraé Crouch

Bless the Lord, O my soul, ____ and all that is with-

in me, Bless His ho - ly ____ Name.

Fine

He has done great things, ____ He has done great things, ____

He has done great things, Bless His ho - ly Name.

D.C. al Fine

14 BIND US TOGETHER

Bob Gillman

Bind us to-ge-ther Lord, Bind us to-ge-ther with

cords that can-not be bro - ken, _____

Bind us to-ge-ther Lord, Bind us to-ge-ther

Bind us to-ge-ther with love _____

Fine

There is on-ly one God. _____

LORD, BE GLORIFIED

15

Words and Music by
Bob Kilpatrick

D.C. al Fine

1. In my life Lord, Be glo-ri-fied, be glo-ri-fied.
2. In my song Lord, Be glo-ri-fied, be glo-ri-fied.
3. In Your church Lord, Be glo-ri-fied, be glo-ri-fied.

In my life Lord, Be glo-ri-fied to-day.
In my song Lord, Be glo-ri-fied to-day.
In Your church Lord, Be glo-ri-fied to-day.

16 BLESSED ASSURANCE

Fanny J. Crosby

Mrs. J. F. Knapp

1. Bless - ed as - sur - ance, Je - sus is mine! __ Oh, what a fore - taste of
2. Per - fect sub - mis - sion, per - fect de - light, __ Vi - sions of rap - ture now
3. Per - fect sub - mis - sion, all is at rest, __ I in my Sav - ior am

glo - ry di - vine! __ Heir of sal - va - tion, pur - chase of God, __
burst on my sight; __ An - gels de - scend - ing, bring from a - bove __
hap - py and blest; __ Watch - ing and wait - ing, look - ing a - bove, __

Born of His Spir - it, washed in His blood. __
Ech - oes of mer - cy, whis - pers of love. __ This is my sto - ry, this is my
Filled with His good - ness, lost in His love. __

song, __ Prais - ing my Sav - ior all the day long; __ This is my sto - ry,

This is my song, —— Prais-ing my Sav - ior all the day long. ——

HEAVENLY SUNSHINE

17

Arr. by Charles E. Fuller

Heav - en - ly sun - shine, heav - en - ly sun - shine, Flood-ing my soul with glo - ry di - vine, —— Heav - en - ly sun - shine, heav - en - ly sun - shine, Hal - le - lu - jah! Je - sus is mine! ——

18 BOOKS OF THE OLD TESTAMENT

Words Arr. by
Mrs. W. I. M. Tabor

Tune: "Did You Ever See A Lassie"
Arr. by Gordon E. Hooker

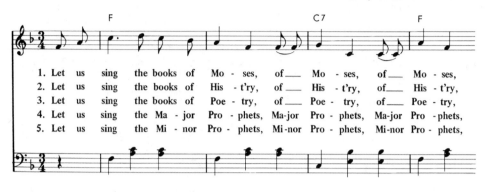

1. Let us sing the books of Mo - ses, of ___ Mo - ses, of ___ Mo - ses,
2. Let us sing the books of His - t'ry, of ___ His - t'ry, of ___ His - t'ry,
3. Let us sing the books of Poe - try, of ___ Poe - try, of ___ Poe - try,
4. Let us sing the Ma - jor Pro - phets, Ma-jor Pro - phets, Major Pro - phets,
5. Let us sing the Mi - nor Pro - phets, Mi-nor Pro - phets, Mi-nor Pro - phets,

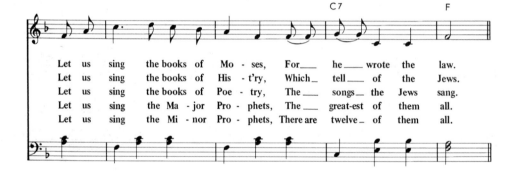

Let us sing the books of Mo - ses, For ___ he ___ wrote the law.
Let us sing the books of His - t'ry, Which ___ tell ___ of the Jews.
Let us sing the books of Poe - try, The ___ songs ___ the Jews sang.
Let us sing the Ma - jor Pro - phets, The ___ great-est of them all.
Let us sing the Mi - nor Pro - phets, There are twelve ___ of them all.

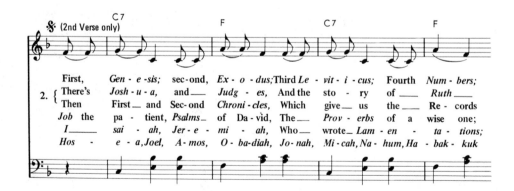

𝄇 (2nd Verse only)

     First, *Gen - e -sis;* sec-ond, *Ex - o - dus;* Third *Le - vit - i - cus;* Fourth *Num - bers;*
2. { There's *Josh - u - a,* and ___ *Judg - es,* And the sto - ry of ___ *Ruth* ___
    Then *First* ___ and Sec-ond *Chroni - cles,* Which give ___ us the ___ Re - cords
Job the pa - tient, *Psalms* ___ of Da - vid, The ___ *Prov - erbs* of a wise one;
I ___ sai - ah, *Jer - e - mi - ah,* Who ___ wrote *Lam - en - ta - tions;*
Hos - e - a, Joel, A - mos, O - ba-diah, Jo - nah, Mi - cah, Na - hum, Ha - bak - kuk

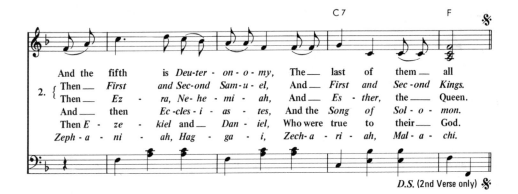

And the fifth   is *Deu-ter - on - o - my,*   The last   of   them   all
2. { Then   *First*   *and Sec-ond Sam-u - el,*   And *First*   *and*   *Sec-ond Kings.*
Then   *Ez*   *ra, Ne- he - mi - ah,*   And *Es - ther,*   the   *Queen.*
And   then   *Ec-cles-i - as - tes,*   And the *Song*   *of*   *Sol - o - mon.*
Then *E - ze - kiel and Dan - iel,*   Who were true   to   their   God.
Zeph - a - ni - ah, Hag - ga - i,   *Zech-a - ri - ah,*   *Mal - a - chi.*

D.S. (2nd Verse only)

JESUS LOVES
THE LITTLE CHILDREN   19

George F. Root

Je - sus loves the lit - tle chil - dren, ___ All the chil - dren of the

world; (the world) Red and yel - low, black and white, They are

pre - cious in His sight; Je - sus loves the lit - tle chil - dren of the world.

20 BREAK FORTH INTO JOY

Unknown

Break forth in-to joy, oh my soul. _____ Break
forth in-to joy, oh my soul. _____ In the
pres-ence of the Lord there is joy for-ev-er more. Break
forth ___ break ___ forth ___ in-to joy oh my soul.

CLEANSE ME

J. Edwin Orr.

Maori Melody, Arranged

1. Search me, O God, and know my heart to - day;
2. I praise Thee, Lord, for cleans - ing me from sin:
3. Lord, take my life, and make it whol - ly Thine;
4. O Ho - ly Ghost, re - viv - al comes from Thee:

Try me, O Sav - ior, know my thoughts, I pray;
Ful - fill Thy Word, and make me pure with - in;
Fill my poor heart with Thy great love di - vine;
Send a re - viv - al start the work in me:

See if there be some wick - ed way in me:
Fill me with fire, where once I burned with shame:
Take all my will, my pas - sion, self and pride;
Thy Word de - clares Thou wilt sup - ply our need:

Cleanse me from ev - 'ry sin and set me free.
Grant my de - sire to mag - ni - fy Thy name.
I now sur - ren - der: Lord, in me a - bide.
For bless - ing now, O Lord, I hum - bly plead.

22 BRIGHTEN THE CORNER
WHERE YOU ARE

Ina Duley Ogdon

Charles H. Gabriel

1. Do not wait un-til some deed of great-ness you may do, Do not
2. Just a-bove are cloud-ed skies that you may help to clear, Let not
3. Here for all your tal-ent you may sure-ly find a need, Here re-

wait to shed your light a-far; To the man-y du-ties ev-er near you
nar-row self your way de-bar; Tho in-to one heart a-lone may fall your
flect the Bright and Morn-ing Star; E-ven from your hum-ble hand the bread of

now be true, Bright-en the cor-ner where you are.
song of cheer, Bright-en the cor-ner where you are. Bright-en the cor-ner
life may feed, Bright-en the cor-ner where you are.

where you are! Bright-en the cor-ner where you are! Some-one far from

har - bor you may guide a - cross the bar, Bright - en the cor - ner where you are!

CHILDREN OF THE
HEAVENLY FATHER

23

Caroline V. Sandell-Berg
Tr., Ernst William Olson

Swedish Melody

1. Chil - dren of the heav'n - ly Fa - ther Safe - ly
2. God his own doth tend and nour - ish, In his
3. Nei - ther life nor death shall ev - er From the
4. Though he giv - eth or he tak - eth, God his

in his bos - om gath - er; Nest - ling bird nor star in
ho - ly courts they flour - ish. From all e - vil things he
Lord his chil - dren sev - er, Un - to them his grace he
chil - dren ne'er for - sak - eth, His the lov - ing pur - pose

heav - en Such a ref - uge e'er was giv - en;
spares them, In his might - y arms he bears them.
show - eth, And their sor - rows all he know - eth.
sole - ly To pre - serve them pure and ho - ly.

24 THE BUTTERFLY SONG

Words and Music by
Brian Howard

1. If I were a but-ter-fly, — I'd thank you, Lord, for
2. If I were an e-le-phant, — I'd thank you, Lord, by
3. If I were a wig-gily worm, — I'd thank you, Lord, that

giv-ing me wings. And if I were a ro-bin in a tree, I'd
rais-ing my trunk. And if I were a kan-ga-roo, you
I could squirm, And if I were a bil-ly-goat, I'd

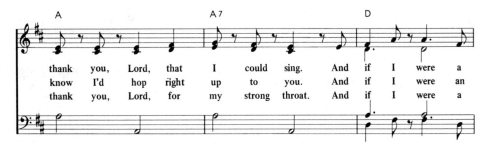

thank you, Lord, that I could sing. And if I were a
know I'd hop right up to you. And if I were an
thank you, Lord, for my strong throat. And if I were a

fish in the sea, — I'd wig-gle my tail and I'd
oct-o-pus, — I'd thank you, Lord, for —
fuz-zy-wuz-zy bear, I'd thank you, Lord, for my

25 CALVARY COVERS IT ALL

Mrs. Walter G. Tayler

1. Far dear-er than all that the world can im-part Was the mes-sage that
2. The stripes that He bore and the thorns that He wore Told His mer-cy and
3. How match-less the grace, when I looked in the face Of Je-sus, my
4. How bless-ed the tho't that my soul by Him bought Shall dwell in the

came to my heart (to my heart), How Je-sus a-lone for my
love ev-er-more (ev-er-more); My heart bowed in shame as I
cru-ci-fied Lord (of my Lord); My re-demp-tion com-plete, I then
glo-ry on high (dwell on high), Where with glad-ness and song I'll be

sin did a-tone, And Cal-va-ry cov-ers it all.
called on His name, And Cal-va-ry cov-ers it all.
found at His feet, And Cal-va-ry cov-ers it all.
one of the throng And Cal-va-ry cov-ers it all.

cov-ers it all.

Chorus

Cal-va-ry cov-ers it all. My past with its sin and stain: My

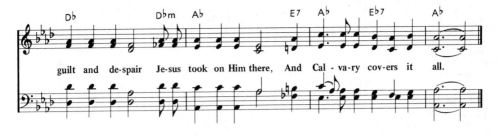

guilt and de-spair Je-sus took on Him there, And Cal-va-ry cov-ers it all.

HAVE THINE OWN WAY 26

Adelaide A. Pollard

G. C. Stebbins

1. Have thine own way, Lord, have thine own way! ___ Thou art the Pot - ter; I am the clay. ___ Mould me and make me Af - ter thy will, ___ While I am wait - ing, Yield - ed and still. ___

2. Have thine own way, Lord, have thine own way! ___ Search me and try me, Mas - ter, to day! ___ Whit - er than snow, Lord, Wash me just now, ___ As in thy pres - ence Hum - bly I bow. ___

3. Have thine own way, Lord, have thine own way! ___ Wound- ed and wea - ry, Help me, I pray! ___ Pow - er, all pow - er, Sure - ly is thine! ___ Touch me and heal me, Sav - ior di - vine! ___

4. Have thine own way, Lord, have thine own way! ___ Hold o'er my be - ing, Ab - so - lute sway! ___ Fill with thy Spir - it, Till all shall see Christ on - ly, al - ways, Liv - ing in me! ___

27   CHARITY

Adapted from I Cor. 13.

Words and Music by
Kenn Gulliksen
Arr. by Henry Wiens

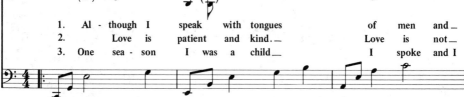

1. Al - though I speak with tongues of men and —
2. Love is patient and kind. — Love is not —
3. One sea - son I was a child — I spoke and I

an - gels —, and though I pro - phe-sy —
en - vi - ous — not proud, but gen - tle and meek —
thought as a child — But when I turn - ed to man —

and un - der - stand all. — Al - though I
seeks not its own way. — Love sings when
such ways put a - side. — Tho' now we

have all faith — so moun -tains may be re - moved
Je - sus pre - vails — Be - lieves and en - dures all things
see thru a glass — yet then we shall see face to face

28 COME AND PRAISE THE LORD

Ps. 118:1-7, 22-23
Steffi Geiser Rubin

Stuart Dauermann

COME BLESS THE LORD

Dale and Evelyn
Hunter

Ps. 134: 1,2

30 COME ON, RING THOSE BELLS

Words and Music by
Andrew Culverwell

1. Ev - 'ry-bod - y likes to take a hol - i - day, __ Ev - 'ry-bod- y likes to take a rest
2. Cel - e - bra -tions come be-cause of some-thing good, __ cele - bra-tions we love to re-call.

spend-ing time to-geth- er with the fam - i - ly, __
Mar - y had a ba - by boy in Beth - le - hem, __ the

shar -ing lots of love__ and hap - pi - ness. _____
great- est cel - e -bra - tion of them all. _____

Come on, ring those bells,

light the Christ-mas tree. __ Je - sus is the King __ born for you and me. __

Come on, ring those bells, ev-'ry-bod-y say, "Je - sus, we re-mem-ber this your birth - day."

AMAZING GRACE 31

John Newton

1. A - maz - ing grace! how sweet the sound, That
2. 'Twas grace that taught my heart to fear, And
3. Thro' man - y dan - gers, toils and snares, I
4. When we've been there ten thou – sand years, Bright

saved a wretch like me! I once ____ was lost, but
grace my fears re - lieved, How pre - cious did that
have al - read - y come; 'Tis grace ____ hath bro't me
shin - ing as the sun, We've no ____ less days to

now ____ am found, Was blind, but now I see.
grace ____ ap - pear The hour I first be - lieved!
safe ____ thus far, And grace will lead me home.
sing ____ God's praise Than when we first be - gun.

32 COME, THOU ALMIGHTY KING

Anonymous

Felice Giardini

4. Come, holy Comforter,
   Thy sacred witness bear
   In this glad hour;
   Thou who almighty art,
   Now rule in every heart,
   And ne'er from us depart,
   Spirit of power!

5. To the great One in Three
   Eternal praises be,
   Hence evermore;
   His sovereign majesty
   May we in glory see,
   And to eternity
   Love and adore.

COME, THOU FOUNT OF EVERY BLESSING

33

Robert Robinson

Asahel Nettleton

1. Come, Thou Fount of ev - 'ry bless - ing, Tune my heart to sing Thy grace;
2. Here I raise my Eb - en - e - zer, Hith- er by Thy help I'm come;
3. O to grace how great a debt - or, Dai - ly I'm con-strained to be;

Streams of mer - cy, nev - er ceas - ing, Call for songs of loud - est praise.
And I hope, by Thy good pleas - ure, Safe - ly to ar - rive at home.
Let that grace now like a fet - ter, Bind my wan - d'ring heart to Thee.

While the hope of end - less glo - ry Fills my heart with joy and love,
Je - sus sought me when a stran - ger, Wand'ring from the fold of God;
Prone to wan - der, Lord, I feel it, Prone to leave the God I love;

Teach me ev - er to a - dore Thee, May I still Thy good - ness prove.
He, to res - cue me from dan - ger, In - ter - posed His pre - cious blood.
Here's my heart, O take and seal it, Seal it for Thy courts a - bove.

34 COMMUNION SONG

Words and Music by
Barry McGuire

1. Take this bread I give to you, And as you do, re-mem-ber me. This bread is my bod-y bro-ken just for you Take it, (take it), eat it: (eat it): Each time you do, re-mem-ber me, re-mem-ber me.

2. Take this cup I fill for you, And as you do, re-mem-ber me. This cup is the new cove-nant I'm mak-ing with you Take it, (take it), drink it: (drink it): Each time you do, re-mem-ber me, re-mem-ber me.

3. Take this love I've giv-en you, And as you do, re-mem-ber

me, re-mem-ber me, re-mem-ber me;

COME TO MY HEART, LORD JESUS

Emily E. S. Elliott

Timothy Richard Matthews

1. Thou didst leave thy throne. And thy king - ly ___ crown When thou
2. Hea - ven's ar - ches ___ rang when the an - gels ___ sang. Pro ___
3. The ___ fox - es found rest and the birds their ___ nest in the
4. Thou ___ cam - est, O Lord, with the liv - ing ___ word, that should
5. When the hea - vens shall ring, and the an - gels ___ sing at thy

cam - est to earth for me, But in Beth - le - hem's home Was there
clai - ming thy roy - al degree; But in low - ly ___ birth didst thou
shade of the for - est tree; But thy couch was the sod, O thou
set thy ___ peo - ple free; But with mock - ing ___ scorn, and with
com - ing to vic - to - ry, Let thy voice call me home, say - ing,

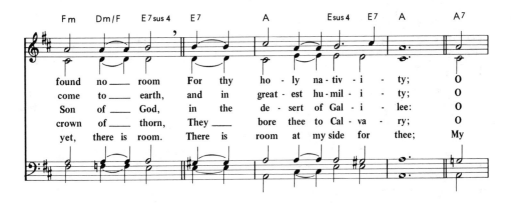

found no ___ room For thy ho - ly na - tiv - i - ty; O
come to ___ earth, and in great - est hu - mil - i - ty; O
Son of ___ God, in the de - sert of Gal - i - lee: O
crown of ___ thorn, They ___ bore thee to Cal - va - ry; O
yet, there is room. There is room at my side for thee; My

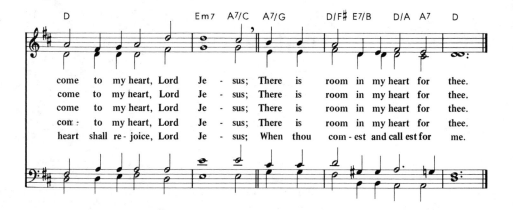

come to my heart, Lord Je - sus; There is room in my heart for thee.
come to my heart, Lord Je - sus; There is room in my heart for thee.
come to my heart, Lord Je - sus; There is room in my heart for thee.
come to my heart, Lord Je - sus; There is room in my heart for thee.
heart shall re - joice, Lord Je - sus; When thou com - est and call est for me.

36   FINALLY HOME

L. E. Singer and Don Wyrtzen

Don Wyrtzen
Arr. by Henry Wiens

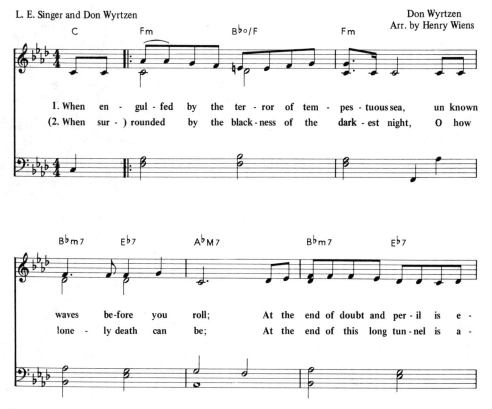

1. When en - gul - fed by the ter - ror of tem - pes - tuous sea, un known
(2. When sur -) rounded by the black - ness of the dark - est night, O how

waves be - fore you roll; At the end of doubt and per - il is e -
lone - ly death can be; At the end of this long tun - nel is a -

37 HOW EXCELLENT IS THY NAME

Words and Music by
Dick Tunney, Melody Tunney
and Paul Smith
Arr. by Henry Wiens

DAY BY DAY

39

Words and Music by
Caroline V. Sandell-Berg

1. Day by day and with each pass-ing mo-ment, Strength I find to
2. Ev-'ry day the Lord him-self is near me, With a spe-cial
3. Help me then, in ev-'ry trib-u-la-tion, So to trust Thy

meet my tri-als here. Trust-ing in my Fa-ther's wise be-stow-ment,
mer-cy for each hour. All my cares He fain would bear and cheer me,
prom-is-es, O Lord, That I lose not faith's sweet con-so-la-tion,

I've no cause for wor-ry or for fear. He whose heart is kind be-yond all
He whose name is Coun-sel-or and Pow'r The pro-tec-tion of His child and
Of-fered me with-in Thy ho-ly Word. Help me, Lord, when toil and trou-ble

meas-ure Gives un-to each day what He deems best, Lov-ing-ly its
treas-ure Is a charge that on him-self He laid. "As thy days, thy
meet-ing, E'er to take, as from a Fa-ther's hand, One by one the

part of pain and plea - sure, Ming-ling toil with peace and __ rest.
strength shall be in meas - ure," This the pledge to me __ He __ made.
days, the mo - ments fleet - ing, Till I reach the prom - ised __ land.

FATHER, I ADORE YOU

40

Words and Music by
Terrye Coelho

1. Fa ther, I a - dore You, Lay my life be -
2. Je sus
3. Spir it

fore You. How I love You;

41 DO, LORD! : PSALM 27

Adapted by J. Y. from Ps. 27, Eph. 3:21

Traditional
Arr. by John Ylvisaker

Do, Lord, O do, Lord, O do re-mem-ber me!

Do, Lord, O do, Lord, O do re-mem-ber me!

Do, Lord, O do, Lord, O do re-mem-ber me! Look a-

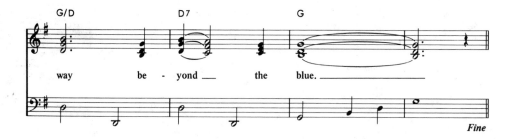

way be-yond ___ the blue. ___

Fine

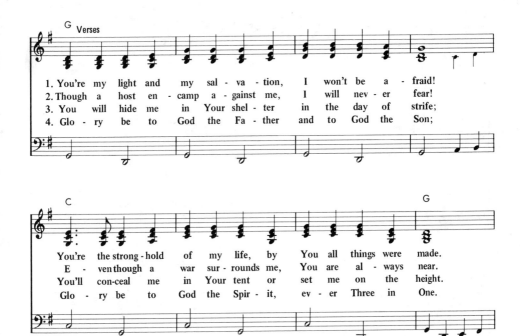

G Verses

1. You're my light and my sal - va - tion, I won't be a - fraid!
2. Though a host en - camp a - gainst me, I will nev - er fear!
3. You will hide me in Your shel - ter in the day of strife;
4. Glo - ry be to God the Fa - ther and to God the Son;

C   G

You're the strong - hold of my life, by You all things were made.
E - ven though a war sur - rounds me, You are al - ways near.
You'll con - ceal me in Your tent or set me on the height.
Glo - ry be to God the Spir - it, ev - er Three in One.

                                                              B7

Foes at - tack me, has - sle me, but I will nev - er
One thing I have asked of You that I will seek for
Now my head is lift - ed up a - bove the storms of
As it was in the be - gin - ning, till our race is

Em   A7   G/D   D7   G

fade, For I move in the strength of the Lord._____
sure Is to live in the house of the Lord._____
night, So I'll sing to the name of the Lord._____
won We can live in the light of the Lord._____

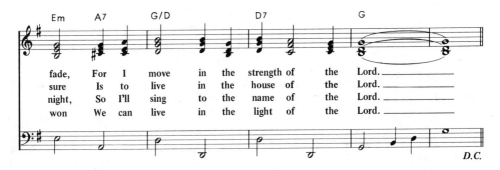

D.C.

EASTER SONG

42

Words and Music by
Anne Herring

1. Hear the bells ring - ing, they're sing - ing that we can be born a - gain!

2. Hear the bells ring - ing, they're sing - ing, "Christ is ris - en from the dead!"

The an - gel up - on the tomb - stone said, — "He is ris - en just as He said,

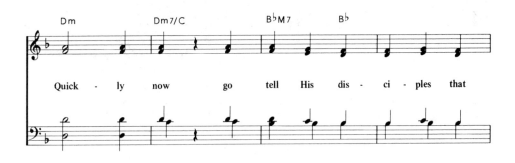

Quick - ly now go tell His dis - ci - ples that

Je - sus Christ is no long - er dead!"

Joy to the world, He is ris - en, Al -

le - lu - ia! He's ris - en, Al - le - lu - ia! He's

ris - en, Al - le - lu - ia!

43 FILL MY CUP, LORD

Words and Music by Richard Blanchard
Arr. by Eugene Clark

1. Like the wom-an at the well I was seek-ing _____ For
2. There are mil-lions in this world who are crav-ing _____ The
3. So my broth-er, if the things this world gave you _____ Leaves

things that could not sat-is-fy. And then I heard my Sav-ior
please-ure earth-ly things af-ford. But none can match the won-drous
hun-gers that won't pass a-way. My bless-ed Lord will come and

speak-ing: "Draw from my well that nev-er shall run dry."
treas-ure _____ That I find in Je-sus Christ, my Lord.
save you _____ If you kneel to Him and hum-bly pray.

Chorus
Fill my cup, Lord,_ I lift it up, Lord._ Come and quench this thirst-ing of my soul.

Bread of heav-en, feed me till I want no more; Fill my cup, fill it up and make me whole.

FATHER, WE THANK YOU 44

John 15:26; I John 4:9,19

Gary Johnson

1. Fa - ther, we thank You; Fa -
2. Je - sus, we thank You; Je -
3. Fa - ther, we love You; Fa -

ther, we thank You for giv - ing to
sus, we thank You for giv - ing to
ther, we thank You be - cause You have

us Your Son; — Fa - ther, we thank You.
us Your Spir - it; Je - sus, we thank You.
first loved us; — Fa - ther, we love You.

45

FOR GOD SO LOVED

John 1:10-12, 3:16-17

Words and Music by
Stuart Dauermann

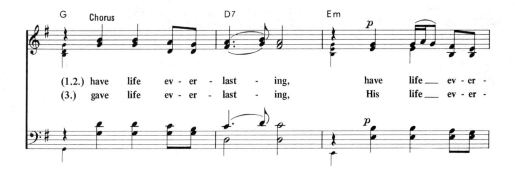

(1.2.) have life ev - er - last - ing, have life ___ ev - er -
(3.) gave life ev - er - last - ing, His life ___ ev - er -

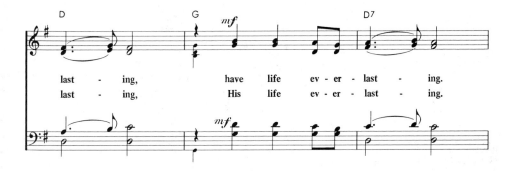

last - ing, have life ev - er - last - ing.
last - ing, His life ev - er - last - ing.

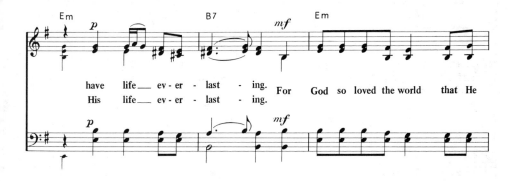

have life ___ ev - er - last - ing. For God so loved the world that He
His life ___ ev - er - last - ing.

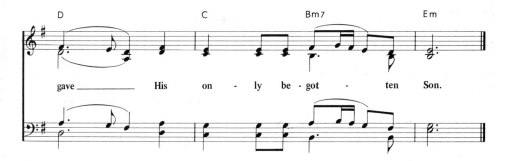

gave _____ His on - ly be - got - ten Son.

46 FOR THOSE TEARS I DIED

Words and Music by
Marsha J. Stevens

1. You said you'd come and share all my sor-rows;
2. Your good-ness so great I can't un-der-stand, And
3. Je-sus, I give you my heart and my soul. I

You said you'd be there for all my to-mor-rows.
dear Lord, I know that all this was planned.
know now with-out God I'd nev-er be whole.

I came so close to send-ing you a-way, But
I know you're here now and al-ways will be. Your
Sav-ior, you o-pened all the right doors, And I

just as you prom-ised you came there to stay,
love loosed my chains and in you I'm free,
thank you and praise you from earth's hum-ble shores,

I just had to pray._____ And Je - sus said,
But Je - sus, why me? _____ And Je - sus said,
Take me, I'm yours._____ And Je - sus said,

"Come to the wa - ter, stand by my side. I know you are

thirst - y, you won't be de - nied._____ I felt ev - ery

tear - drop when in dark - ness you cried,_____ And I

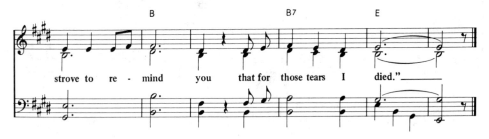

strove to re - mind you that for those tears I died."_____

47 FREELY, FREELY

Adapted from Matt. 10:7, 8

Words and Music by
Carol Owens

1. God for - gave my sin in Je - sus' name, I've been born a -
2. All pow'r is giv'n in Je - sus' name, In earth and

gain in Je - sus' name; And in Je - sus' name I come to you To
heav'n in Je - sus' name; And in Je - sus' name I come to you To

Chorus

share His love as He told me to. He said, "Free - ly, free - ly
share His pow'r as He told me to.

you have re - ceived: Free - ly, free - ly give. Go in my

name, and, be - cause you be - lieve, Oth - ers will know that I live."

GENTLE LIKE YOU 48

Words and Music by
Charles F. Brown

1. Je - sus, Je - sus, Ru - ler of might - y men;
2. Je - sus, Je - sus, Friend to the lone - ly soul;
3. Je - sus, Je - sus, Shep - herd of wan - d'ring ones;
4. Je - sus, Je - sus, Sav - ior of trou - bled man;

Je - sus, Je - sus, Make me gen - tle like You.
Je - sus, Je - sus, Love my broth - er thro' me.
Je - sus, Je - sus, Guide me thro' the dark night.
Je - sus, Je - sus, Give me peace in my soul.

49 GLORIFY THY NAME

Words and Music by Donna Adkins
Arranged by Edward Dagnes

1. Fa - ther, we love Thee, we praise Thee, we a - dore Thee.
2. Je - sus,
3. Spir - it,

Glo - ri - fy Thy name in all the earth. _____

Glo - ri - fy Thy name, glo - ri - fy Thy name.

Glo - ri - fy Thy name in all the earth. _____

GOD CALLING YET! SHALL I NOT HEAR

50

Gerhard Tersteegen
Tr. Sarah Findlater

Henry K. Oliver

5. Ah, yield Him all; in Him confide:
   Where but with Him doth peace abide?
   Break loose, let earthly bonds be riven,
   And let the spirit rise to heav'n!

6. God calling yet! - I cannot stay;
   My heart I yield without delay:
   Vain world, farewell! from thee I part;
   The voice of God hath reached my heart!

51 GREAT AND WONDERFUL

Rev. 15:3-4

Words and Music by
Stuart Dauermann

1. Great and won-der-ful ___ are Thy won-drous deeds, ___ O Lord God, the Al-might-y. ___ Just and true ___ are ___ all Thy ways, O Lord; ___ King of the a-ges art Thou. ___

2. All the na-tions shall ___ come and wor-ship Thee, ___ For Thy glo-ry shall be re-vealed. ___ Hal-le-lu-jah! ___ Hal-le-lu-jah! ___ Hal-le-lu-jah! A-

2nd time to Coda

Who shall not fear and

glo - ri - fy   Thy_____ name,   O   Lord?_____

For   Thou   a - lone   art   ho - ly,   Thou_____

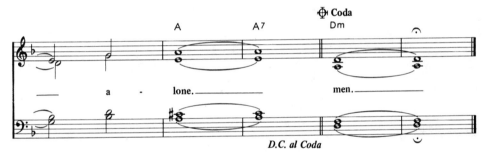

⊕ Coda

____ a - lone._____   men.

D.C. al Coda

GOD IS SO GOOD

52

African melody

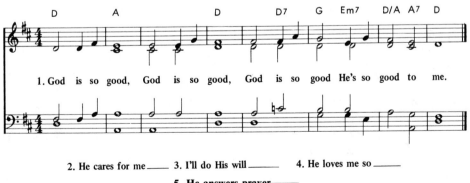

1. God is so good, God is so good, God is so good He's so good to me.

2. He cares for me____   3. I'll do His will____   4. He loves me so____

5. He answers prayer———

53 GREAT IS THE LORD

Psalm 48:1

Robert Ewing

Great is the Lord and great-ly to be praised.___ In the

cit-y of our God, in the moun-tain of His ho-li-ness.

Beau-ti-ful for sit-u-a-tion,___ the joy of the whole earth,

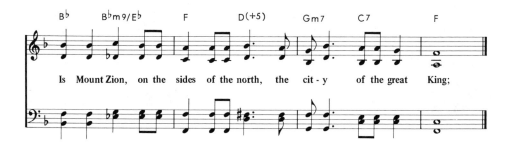

Is Mount Zion, on the sides of the north, the cit-y of the great King;

GROWING TOGETHER

54

Bob Laurent, Ralph Hunt, Kathy Brawley,
Pam Murphy and Mark Johnson

Grow-ing to-geth-er,— lov-ing one an-oth-er,— grow-ing to-geth-er— in the Lord, in the Lord.

1. His love be-comes our own, by dy-ing on mount Cal-var-y, we love not as the world loves, but in Him.—

2. I'm waiting for the day, I can look at Him and say;
"Father, I thank you for your love."
CHORUS

3. It's in dying that we live, by giving we receive,
and growing become children of the light and the day.
CHORUS

55 GREAT IS THY FAITHFULNESS

Thomas Chisholm

William Runyan

1. "Great is Thy faith - ful - ness," O God my Fa - ther,
2. Sum - mer and win - ter, and spring - time and har - vest,
3. Par - don for sin and a peace that en - dur - eth,

There is no shad - ow of turn - ing with Thee;
Sun, moon and stars in their cours - es a - bove,
Thy own dear pres - ence to cheer and to - guide;

Thou chang - est not, Thy com - pas - sions, they fail not;
Join with all na - ture in man - i - fold wit - ness
strength for to - day and bright hope for to - mor - row,

As Thou hast been Thou for - ev - er wilt be.
To Thy great faith - ful - ness, mer - cy and love.
Bless - ings all mine, with ten thou - sand be - side!

"Great is Thy faith-ful-ness! Great is Thy faith-ful-ness!"
Morn-ing by morn-ing new mer-cies I see;
All I have need-ed Thy hand hath pro-vid-ed
"Great is Thy faith-ful-ness," Lord, un-to me!

THE B-I-B-L-E 56

The B - I - B - L - E, Yes, that's the book for me; I
stand a - lone on the Word of God; The B - I - B - L - E.

57 HALLOWED BE THY NAME

Adapted from Matt. 6:9-13

Traditional West Indian Melody
Arr. by Lyndell Leathermann

1. Our Fa - ther who art in heav - en,
2. As in heav - en, so on the earth.
3. And for - give us all our debts;
4. Lead us not in to temp - ta - tion;
5. Thine is the king - dom, the pow - er, and the glo - ry;
6. A - men, it shall be so.

Hal-low-ed be Thy name.

Thy king - dom come, Thy
Give us this day our
Just as we for -
But de - liv - er
For - ev - er and for -
A - men, a - men, it

will be done;
dai - ly bread.
give our debt - ors.
us from e - vil.
ev - er - more.
shall be so.

Hal-low-ed be Thy name.

Hal-low - ed be Thy name.

HE GAVE ME BEAUTY FOR ASHES 58

Adapted from Isaiah 61:3

Unknown
Arr. by Tom Fettke

He gave me beau-ty for ash-es, the

oil of joy for mourn-ing, The gar-ment of

praise for the spir-it of heav-i-ness; That we might be

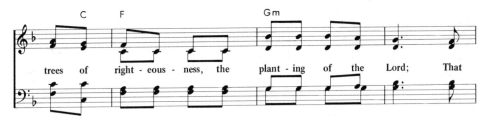

trees of right-eous-ness, the plant-ing of the Lord; That

He might be glo-ri-fied.

59 THE TREES OF THE FIELD

Isaiah (Adapted by Steffi Geiser Rubin)

Stuart Dauermann
Arr. by Henry Wiens

field will clap their hands, — The trees of the field will

clap their hands. — The trees of the field will clap their hands,

— while you go out with joy. You shall go

HE IS LORD

60

Based on Phil. 2:11

Traditional

He is Lord, He is Lord! He is ris - en from the dead, and He is

Lord! Ev-'ry knee shall bow, ev-'ry tongue con - fess That Je - sus Christ is Lord.

61 HE LIVES

Words and Music by
A. H. Ackley

1. I serve a ris - en Sav - ior, he's in the world to-day; ___ I know that he is liv - ing, what-ev - er men may say; ___ I see his hand of mer - cy, I hear his voice of cheer, ___ And just the time I need him ___ he's al - ways near. ___

2. In all the world a - round me I see his lov - ing care, ___ And though my heart grows wea - ry I nev - er will de - spair; ___ I know that he is lead - ing, through all the storm - y blast, ___ The day of his ap - pear - ing ___ will come at last. ___

3. Re - joice, re - joice, O Chris - tian, lift up your voice and sing ___ E - ter - nal hal - le - lu - jahs to Je - sus Christ the King! ___ The Hope of all who seek him, the Help of all who find, ___ None oth - er is so lov - ing, ___ so good and kind. ___ He

lives, _____ he lives, _____ Christ Je - sus lives __ to -

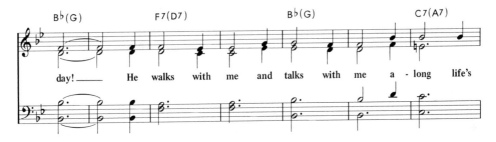

day! ___ He walks with me and talks with me a - long life's

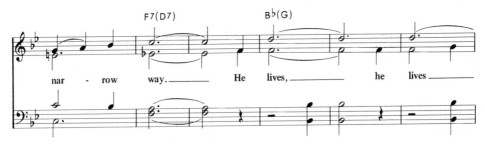

nar - row way. _____ He lives, _____ he lives _____

___ sal - va - tion to im - part! _____ You ask me

how I know he lives? He lives with - in my heart. _____

62   HE RESTORETH MY SOUL

Words and Music by
Margaret Zilch

1. The Lord is my shep-herd I need him, When wea-ry and torn on life's way; His oil is a balm for my heal-ing, His rod and His staff are my stay.

2. In shad-y green pas-tures He feeds me, And there I shall rest in His care; By cool flow-ing wa-ters He leads me, And noth-ing can trou-ble me there.

3. His good-ness and mer-cy are with me, They fol-low me all my life through; With joy I will face each to-mor-row, Till heav-n's green pas-tures I view.

63 HE THE PEARLY GATES WILL OPEN

Fred Blom

Elsie Ahlwen
by W. Elmo Mercer

1. Love Di-vine, so great and won - drous, Deep and might - y, pure, sub - lime;
2. Like a dove when hunt - ed fright - ened, As a wound-ed fawn was I;
3. Love Di-vine, so great and won - drous, All my sins He then for - gave;
4. In life's e - ven - tide, at twi - light, At His door I'll knock and wait;

Com - ing from the heart of Je - sus, Just the same thro' tests of time.
Bro - ken-heart-ed yet He healed me, He will heed the sin - ner's cry.
I will sing His praise for - ev - er, For His blood, His pow'r to save.
By the pre-cious love of Je - sus, I shall en - ter heav-en's gate.

He the pearl - y gates will o - pen, So that I may en - ter in;

For he pur-chased my re - demp - tion, and for - gave me all my sin.

HEART SONG

64

Tim Newton

65 HE'S EVERYTHING TO ME

Words and Music by
Ralph Carmichael

1. In the stars His hand-i-work I see, On the wind He speaks with maj-es-ty; Though He rul-eth o-ver land and sea, What is that to me?
2. I will cel-e-brate Na-tiv-i-ty, For it has a place in his-to-ry; Sure, He came to set His pro-ple free What is that to me?

Till by faith I met Him face to face And I felt the

66 GREAT IS THE LORD

Words and Music by
Michael W. Smith and Deborah D. Smith
Arr. by Henry Wiens

67 HEAVENLY FATHER, I APPRECIATE YOU

Unknown

Heav-en-ly Fa - ther, I ap - pre - ci - ate You.

Heav-en-ly Fa - ther, I ap - pre - ci - ate You.

I love You, a - dore You, I bow down be -

fore You. Heav-en-ly Fa - ther, I ap - pre - ci - ate You.

HERE WE ARE

Words and Music by
Dallas Holm

Here we are, ____ in Your pres - ence,

lift - ing ho - ly hands ____ to you. ____

Here we are, ____ prais - ing Je - sus

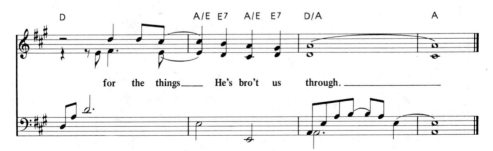

for the things ____ He's bro't us through. ____

69 HIS BANNER OVER ME IS LOVE

Adapted from Ps. 40:2;
Song 2:4; John 5:5

Unknown
Arr. by Lyndell Leatherman

Anonymous

1. I'm feast-ing at His ban-quet-ing ta-ble; His ban-ner o-ver me is love. I'm feast-ing at His ban-quet-ing ta-ble; His ban-ner o-ver me is love. I'm feast-ing at His ban-quet-ing ta-ble; His ban-ner o-ver me is love, His

2. He placed my feet on the firm foun-da-tion; His ban-ner o-ver me is love. He placed my feet on the firm foun-da-tion; His ban-ner o-ver me is love. He placed my feet on the firm foun-da-tion; His ban-ner o-ver me is love, His

3. He is the vine and we are the branch-es; His ban-ner o-ver me is love. He is the vine and we are the branch-es; His ban-ner o-ver me is love. He is the vine and we are the branch-es; His ban-ner o-ver me is love, His

4. I'm my beloved's and He is mine, His banner over me is love . . .

5. He lifts me up to the heavenly places, His banner over me is love . . .

6. One way to peace through the power of the cross, His banner over me is love. . . .

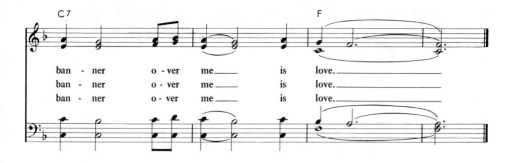

ban - ner   o - ver   me____   is   love.____
ban - ner   o - ver   me____   is   love.____
ban - ner   o - ver   me____   is   love.____

BLESS THE LORD, O MY SOUL   70

Adapted from Ps. 103:1

Unknown

Bless   the Lord,   O   my   soul;   Bless the Lord,   O   my   soul;

And   all   that is   with - in   me   bless His   ho - ly   name.

71 HIS EYE IS ON THE SPARROW

Civilla D. Martin

Charles H. Gabriel.

1. Why should I feel dis-cour-aged, __ Why should the shad-ows come, __
2. "Let not your heart be troub-led," __ His ten-der word I hear, __
3. When-ev-er I am tempt-ed, __ When-ev-er clouds a-rise, __

Why should my heart be lone-ly. __ And long for heav'n and home, __ When
And rest-ing on His good-ness, __ I lose my doubts and fears; __ Tho'
When song gives place to sigh-ing, __ When hope with-in me dies, __ I

Je-sus is my por-tion? __ My con-stant friend is He: __ His
by the path He lead-eth, __ But one step I may see: __ His
draw the clos-er to Him, __ From care He sets me free: __ His

eye is on the spar-row, __ And I know He watch-es me; __ His
eye is on the spar-row, __ And I know He watch-es me; __ His
eye is on the spar-row, __ And I know He cares-for me; __ His

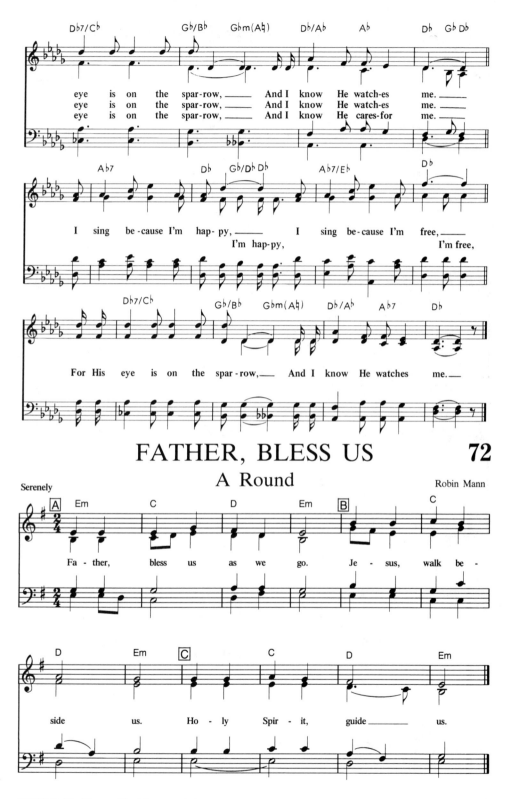

FATHER, BLESS US

A Round

Robin Mann

73   HIS NAME IS WONDERFUL

Audrey Mieir

His name is won-der-ful, His name is won-der-ful, His name is won-der-ful, Je - sus my Lord. He is the might-y King; Mas - ter of ev -'ry-thing; His name is won-der-ful,

Je - sus my Lord. He's the great shep - herd, the

rock of all a - ges. Al - might - y God is

He. _____ Bow down be - fore Him,

love and a - dore Him, His name is

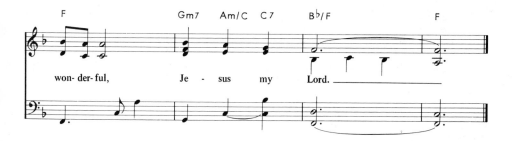

won- der- ful, Je - sus my Lord. _____

HOLY, HOLY

74

Words and Music by
Jimmy Owens

1. Ho - ly, ho - ly, ho-ly, ho - ly,___ Ho-ly, ho - ly,___ Lord God Al - might - y; And we lift our hearts be - fore You as a tok-en of our love, Ho - ly, ho - ly, ho-ly ho - ly.
2. Gra - cious Fa - ther, Gra-cious Fa - ther,___ We're so blest to be Your__ chil - dren, Gra-cious Fa - ther; And we lift our heads be - fore You as a tok-en of our love, Gra-cious Fa - ther, Gra-cious Fa - ther.
3. Pre - cious Je - sus, Pre-cious Je - sus,___ We're so glad that You've re - deemed us, Pre-cious Je - sus; And we lift our hands be - fore You as a tok-en of our love, Pre-cious Je - sus, Pre-cious Je - sus.
4. Ho - ly Spir - it, Ho - ly Spir - it,___ Come and fill our hearts a - new,___ Ho - ly Spir - it; And we lift our voice be - fore You as a tok-en of our love, Ho - ly Spir - it, Ho - ly Spir - it.
5. Hal - le - lu - jah, Hal-le - lu - jah,___ Hal - le - lu - jah,___ Hal - le - lu - jah; And We lift our hearts be - fore You as a tok-en of our love, Hal - le - lu - jah, Hal - le - lu - jah.

CATCH THE VISION

Sandy Knoernschild

Arr. by John Rutter

1. O ev-'ry-one of ea-ger heart, God's mes-sage to the world im-
2. All Christ-en-dom now hear His Word And let your hearts with-in be
3. Sons, rise to arms fear not the foe! With roy-al ban-ners for-ward
4. Let Je-sus' work your plea-sure be, Say, "Here am I, send me, send

part.
stirred. Catch the vi-sion of His mis-sion, Pro-claim how Je-sus lived and
go. To ev-'ry na-tion, ev-'ry
me!" He sets His will be-fore your
Let not the an-swer heard from

died That man might thus be jus-ti-fied;
place, Be thou a ves-sel of His grace.
eyes, And proves His law is good and wise. Catch the vi-sion of His
you Be, "There is noth-ing I can do."

Refrain

mis-sion, Catch the vi-sion of his mis-sion, Al-le-lu-ia!

HOLY SPIRIT,
THOU ART WELCOME

Dottie Rambo
and David Huntsinger

HOW GREAT IS OUR GOD

Anonymous

How great is our God, _____ How great is His Name. How great is our God _____ for-ever the same! _____ He rolled back the wa-ters_____ _____ of the might-y Red Sea, _____ And He said "I'll nev-er leave you,_____ Put your trust in me! _____

78 HOW GREAT THOU ART

Stuart K. Hine

Swedish Melody

1. O Lord my God! When I in awe-some won-der Con-sid-er
2. When through the woods and for-est glades I wan-der And hear the
3. And when I think that God, His son not spar-ing, Sent Him to
4. When Christ shall come with shout of ac-cla-ma-tion And take me

all the worlds Thy hands have made, — I see the stars, I hear the roll-ing
birds sing sweet-ly in the trees; — When I look down from loft-y moun-tain
die, I scarce can take it in; — That on the cross, my bur-den glad-ly
home, what joy shall fill my heart! — Then I shall bow in hum-ble ado-

thun-der, Thy pow'r through out the un-i-verse dis-played, —
gran-deur, And hear the brook and feel the gen-tle breeze; —
bear-ing, He bled and died to take a-way my sin; —
ra-tion And there pro-claim, my God, how great Thou art! —

Refrain

Then sings my soul, my Sav-ior God to Thee; — How great Thou

A SONG OF PRAISE 79

Words and Music by John Worre

Sing a song of praise un-to the Lord.

Sing it out and Let your voice be heard. He's the

King of kings up on the thrones, He's the

HYMN OF JOY

Gladys I. Pearson

Vicki Vogel Schumidt

1. Oh, Lord, my God, Shin - ing in cre - a - tion
2. Oh, Lord, my God, King of ev - 'ry na - tion
3. Oh, Lord, my God, Spi - rit in - spir - a - tion

In moun - tains tall, In leaf, in air, in sea.
You came to earth To die to set me free.
My com - fort now And all the years to be.

Let ev - 'ry breeze Break forth in ad - u - la - tion
Let ev - 'ry voice Sing forth in ac - cla - ma - tion
Let ev - 'ry heart Bow down in a - dor - a - tion

And sing a hymn of joy to Thee! _____
And sing a hymn of joy to Thee! _____
And sing a hymn of joy to Thee! _____

* Arpeggiate left hand for accompaniment.

81 I AM JESUS' LITTLE LAMB

Henrietta L. von Hayn
Tr. Composite

Brüder Choral-Buch

1. I am Jesus' little lamb, Ev - er
2. Day by day, at home, a - way, Je - sus
3. Who so hap - py as I am, E - ven

glad at heart I am; For my Shep - herd gent - ly
is my staff and stay. When I hun - ger, Je - sus
now the Shep - herd's lamb? And when my short life is

guides me, Knows my need and well pro - vides me; Loves me
feeds me, In - to pleas - ant pas - tures leads me; When I
end - ed, By his an - gel host at - tend - ed, He shall

ev - 'ry day the same, E - ven calls me by my name.
thirst, he bids me go Where the qui - et wa - ters flow.
fold me to his breast, There with - in his arms to rest.

I AM COVERED OVER

Unknown

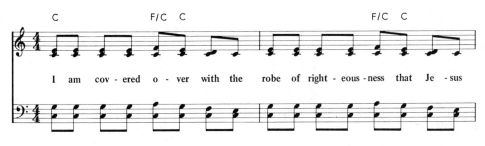

I am cov-ered o-ver with the robe of right-eous-ness that Je - sus

gives to me,— (gives to me,)— I am cov-ered o-ver with the

pre-cious blood of Je-sus and He lives in me,— (lives in me,)—

Oh, what a joy it is to know, my Heav-en-ly Fa-ther loves me so, He

gives to me. — My Je - sus, when He looks at me, He sees not

what I used to be, but He sees Je - sus.

83 GREATER IS HE THAT IS IN ME

I John 4:4

Lanny Wolfe

Great - er is He — that is in me, Great - er is He — that is in me,

Great - er is He — that is in me than he that is in — the world!

I AM LOVED

84

Words and Music by
William J. Gaither
Arr. Henry Wiens

(1.2) I am loved, I am loved, I can risk lov-ing
(3) You are loved, You are loved, You can risk lov-ing

you, For the One____ who knows me best loves me most.
too, For the One____ who knows you best loves you most.

I am loved, you are loved, Won't you please take my
I am loved, we are loved, Won't you please take our

hand? We are free to love each oth-er We are loved!
hand? We are free to love each oth-er We are loved!

SLOW DOWN

85

Chuck Girard
Arr. by Henry Wiens

I HAVE CALLED YOU BY NAME 86

Words and Music by
Gloria Lien

"I have called you by name you are mine," says the Lord. I have called you by name
Do not be a-fraid; I have called you by name. Be not a-fraid; I am your God, I am
with you.

1. When you pass through deep wat - ers, I will be with you. Your
2. Do not lose hope or cour - age; I will be with you. My

Fine

trou - bles will not over — whelm you when you pass through the fire
pres - ence will be ⅞ your strength each day when temp ta - tions o'er whelm

You will not be burned; The trials will not hurt you. I have
You will not give in; The trials will not hurt you. I have

D.S.

87 I HAVE DECIDED
TO FOLLOW JESUS

As Sung in Assam, India

Folk melody from India
Arr. N. J.

1. I have de - cid - ed _____ to fol - low Je - sus, _____
2. Tho no one join me, _____ still I will fol - low, _____
3. The world be - hind me, _____ the cross be - fore me, _____

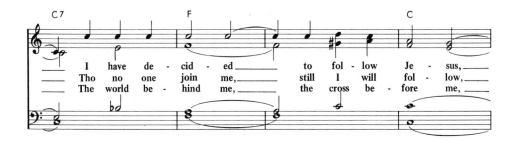

_____ I have de - cid - ed _____ to fol - low Je - sus, _____
_____ Tho no one join me, _____ still I will fol - low, _____
_____ The world be - hind me, _____ the cross be - fore me, _____

_____ I have de - cid - ed _____ to fol - low Je - sus _____ No turn - ing
_____ Tho no one join me, _____ still I will fol - low _____ No turn - ing
_____ The world be - hind me, _____ the cross be - fore me _____ No turn - ing

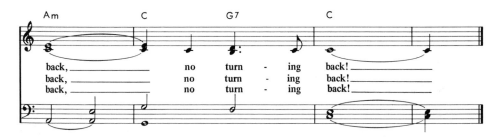

back, _____ no turn - ing back! _____
back, _____ no turn - ing back! _____
back, _____ no turn - ing back! _____

4. Take the whole world but give me Jesus, ... I'll follow Him, I'll follow Him.

I KNOW NOW 88

Words and Music by
Ray Hildebrand
Arr. by Henry Wiens

1. Born in a little man-ger low down in the back-side of Beth - le-hem one star - ry nite; Born to a mai - den named Ma - ry, car - pen - ter Jo - seph that star - ry nite; Some said He was nothin' but a Ba - by, born to a poor man that star - ry nite; Some said He was God puttin' on skin and walk-in' a-mong

2. Three wise men from a - far fol - lowed that star they knew who He was; Why did the shep-herds bow down with the sheep on the ground they knew who He was; Why did the King named He - rod kill all the ba - bies, he knew who He was; Why did the an - gels sing to the boy baby

FEED US NOW

89

Robin Mann

Unhurried

1. Feed us now, Bread of life, In this ho - ly meal;
2. Piece of bread, glass of wine: Lord, this food is good!
3. God is here, O so near; Near - er than our thoughts.

Let us know your love a - new; We hun - ger _ for you.
Love and mer - cy come to us; Your prom - ise _ we trust.
Stay with us where - 'er we go; Lord, help us _ to grow.

Feed us now, Bread of life, Come and live with - in;
Piece of bread, glass of wine; Who can un - der - stand
God is here, O so near, In this heav - en's meal.

Verses 1., 2. **Verse 3**

Let your peace be ours to-day, Lord Je - sus, we pray.
How His mer - cy works in these? Yet, Lord, we be - lieve.
May we al - ways feed on you - On the bread that is true.

90

I KNOW THAT
MY REDEEMER LIVES

Samuel Medley

John Hatton

1. I know that my Re - deem - er lives!
2. He lives to bless me with His love,
3. He lives to grant me rich sup - ply,
4. He lives to si - lence all my fears,
5. He lives all glo - ry to His name!

What com - fort this sweet sen - tence gives!
He lives to plead for me a - bove,
He lives to guide me with His eye,
He lives to wipe a - way my tears,
He lives, my Je - sus still the same;

He lives, He lives, Who once was dead,
He lives, my hun - gry soul to feed,
He lives to com - fort me when faint,
He lives to calm my trou - bled heart,
O the sweet joy this sen - tence gives:

He lives, my ev - er - liv - ing Head.
He lives to help in time of need.
He lives to hear my soul's com - plaint.
He lives all bless - ings to im - part.
I know that my Re - deem - er lives!

I LAY MY SINS ON JESUS

Horatius Bonar

Greek Melody

1. I lay my sins on Je - sus, The spot -less Lamb of God;
2. I lay my wants on Je - sus, All full- ness dwells in Him;
3. I long to be like Je - sus, Meek, lov - ing, low - ly, mild;

He bears them all and frees us From the ac-curs-ed load.
He heals all my dis - eas - es, He doth my soul re - deem.
I long to be like Je - sus, The Fa - ther's ho - ly Child.

I bring my guilt to Je - sus, To wash my crim - son stains.
I lay my griefs on Je - sus, My bur - dens and my cares:
I long to be with Je - sus, A - mid the heav'n - ly throng,

White in His blood most pre - cious, Till not a spot re - mains.
He from them all re - leas - es, He all my sor - rows shares.
To sing with saints His prais - es, To learn the an - gels' song.

92 I LOOK NOT BACK

Annie Johnson Flint

Oskar Ahnfelt

1. I look not back; God knows the fruit-less ef - forts, The wast - ed
2. I look not for - ward; God sees all the fu - ture, The road that,
3. I look not round me; then would fears as - sail me, So wild the

hours, the sin - ning, the re - grets. I leave them all with Him who blots the
short or long, will lead me home, And He will face with me its ev - 'ry
tu - mult of earth's rest-less seas, So dark the world, so filled with woe and

rec - ord, And gra - cious - ly for - gives, and then for - gets.
tri - al, And bear for me the bur - dens that may come.
e - vil, So vain the hope of com - fort and of ease. A - men.

I look not inward; that would make me wretched;
For I have naught on which to stay my trust.
Nothing I see save failures and shortcomings,
And weak endeavors, crumbling into dust.

But I look up - into the face of Jesus,
For there my heart can rest, my fears are stilled;
And there is joy, and love, and light for darkness,
And perfect peace, and every hope fulfilled.

I LOVE TO TELL THE STORY 93

Katherine Henkey

William G. Fischer

1. I love to tell the sto - ry Of un - seen things a - bove,
2. I love to tell the sto - ry; How pleas - ant to re - peat
3. I love to tell the sto - ry; For those who know it best

Of Je - sus and His glo - ry, Of Je - sus and His love.
What seems, each time I tell it, More won - der - ful - ly sweet.
Seem hun - ger - ing and thirst - ing To hear it, like the rest.

I love to tell the sto - ry, Be - cause I know 'tis true;
I love to tell the sto - ry, For some have nev - er heard
And when, in scenes of glo - ry, I sing the new, new song,

It sat - is - fies my long - ings As noth - ing else could do.
The mes - sage of sal - va - tion From God's own ho - ly Word.
'Twill be the old, old sto - ry, That I have loved so long.

Chorus Eb   Eb7   Eb7/Ab Ab   Db   Ab

I love to tell the sto-ry, 'Twill be my theme in glo-ry

Db   Ab   Eb7 Ab

To tell the old,, old sto-ry Of Je-sus and His love.

94   COME INTO HIS PRESENCE

Ps. 100:2, Rom. 10:9, Rev. 5:12   Unknown

1 C   G   2 C   F   G   C

Come in-to His presen-ce sing-ing   Al - le - lu - ia
Praise the Lord to-geth-er sing-ing   Je - sus is Lord,
                                       Wor - thy the Lamb,
                                       Glo - ry to God,

3 F   C   4 Dm   G   C

Al - le - lu - ia,   Al - le - lu - ia.
Je - sus is Lord,   Je - sus is Lord.
wor - thy the Lamb,   wor - thy the Lamb.
glo - ry to God,   glo - ry to God.

*can by sung as a four-part round.

I SAW THE LORD

95

Adapted from Isaiah 6:1, 3

Unknown
Arr. by Tom Fettke

96   I WILL SING OF THE MERCIES

Adapted from Psalm 89:1

Unknown
Arr. by David Cole

I will sing of the mer-cies of the Lord for-ev-er, I will

1. sing. I will sing. 2.3. sing of the mer-cies of the

Lord. With my mouth will I make known Thy

Fine

faith-ful-ness, Thy faith-ful-ness. With my mouth will I make

known Thy faith-ful-ness to all gen-er-a-tions.

D.C. al Fine

I WILL SERVE THEE

97

William J. & Gloria Gaither

William J. Gaither

Slowly, with expression

I will serve Thee _____ be-cause I love Thee, _____ You have given life to me; _____ I was nothing _____ be-fore You found me, _____ You have

IN HIS TIME

Adapted by D.B. from Eccles 3:11

Diane Ball

1. In His time (in His time), in His time (in His time),
2. In Your time (in Your time), in Your time (in Your time),

He makes all things beau - ti - ful in His time (in His time).
You make all things beau - ti - ful in Your time (in Your time).

Lord, please show me ev - 'ry day as You're teach - ing me Your way,
Lord, my life to You I bring; May each song I have to sing.

That You do just what You say in Your time (in Your time).
Be to You a love - ly thing in Your time (in Your time).

99 I WILL SING UNTO THE LORD

Exodus 15:1,2

Unknown

I will sing un - to the Lord __ for He hath tri - umphed glo - rious - ly. __ The

horse and rid - er thrown in - to the sea. I will sing un - to the Lord __ for

He hath tri - umphed glo - rious - ly. __ The horse and rid - er thrown in - to the sea. The

Lord, my God, my strength, my song has now be - come my vic - to -

ry. The Lord, my God, my strength, my song, has now be - come my vic - to -

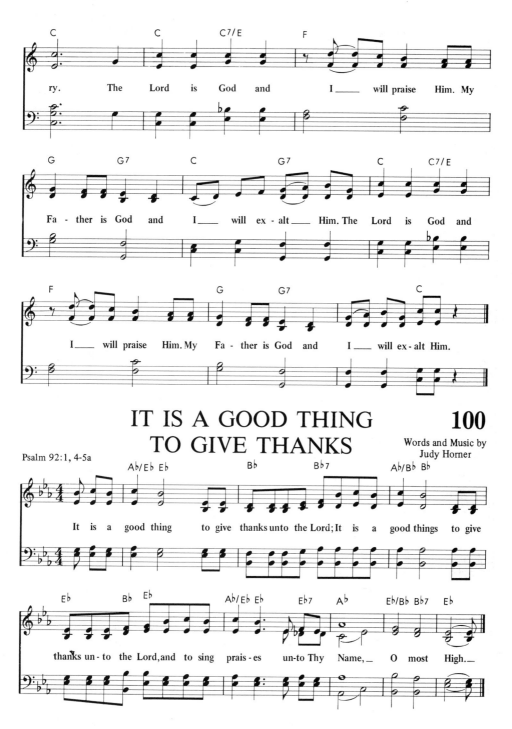

ry.   The   Lord   is   God   and   I___   will praise   Him. My

Fa - ther is God   and   I___   will ex - alt___   Him. The   Lord   is   God   and

I___   will praise Him. My   Fa - ther is God   and   I ___ will ex - alt Him.

IT IS A GOOD THING
TO GIVE THANKS

100

Words and Music by
Judy Horner

Psalm 92:1, 4-5a

It is a   good thing   to give thanks unto the Lord; It   is   a   good things   to give

thanks un - to the Lord, and to sing prais - es   un - to Thy Name, __ O most High. __

101 I'D RATHER HAVE JESUS

Rhea F. Miller

George Beverly Shea

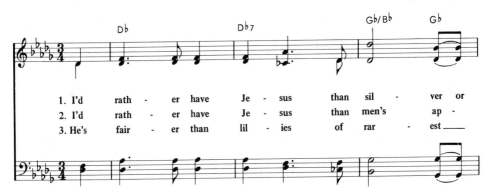

1. I'd rath - er have Je - sus than sil - ver or
2. I'd rath - er have Je - sus than men's ap -
3. He's fair - er than lil - ies of rar - est___

gold, I'd rath - er be His than have rich - es un -
plause, I'd rath - er be faith - ful to His___ dear
bloom, He's sweet - er than hon - ey from out___ the

told; I'd rath - er have Je - sus than hous - es or
cause; I'd rath - er have Je - sus than world - wide
comb; He's all that my hun - ger - ing spir - it

102 IF MY PEOPLE WILL PRAY

Adapted by J.O. from II Chron 7:14

Jimmy Owens

103   IN THY PRESENCE, LORD

Words and Music by
Tom Elie

In Thy pres - ence, Lord,_____ In Thy pres - ence, Lord, _____

_____ I de - sire to be con - tin - ual - ly in Thy

pres - ence, Lord. _____ As I lift my hands be - fore You I lay

down all my am - bi - tions. I just de - sire to be con -

tin - ual - ly in Thy pres - ence, Lord.

INTO THY PRESENCE

104

Unknown
Titus 3:5

Unknown
Arr. by Lyndell Leatherman

105 IT IS NO SECRET
(What God Can Do)

Words and Music by
Stuart Hamblen

106 IT IS WELL WITH MY SOUL

H. G. Spafford

Phillip P. Bliss

IT'S NO LONGER I
THAT LIVETH

107

Adapted from Gal. 2:20

Sally Ellis
Arr. by Lyndell Leatherman

It's no long - er I _____ that liv - eth, _____ But

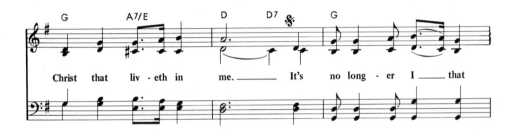

Christ that liv - eth in me. _____ It's no long - er I _____ that

liv - eth, _____ But Christ that liv - eth in me. He

Fine

lives, He lives, Je - sus is a - live in me.

D.S. al Fine

108 I'VE GOT PEACE LIKE A RIVER

Spiritual based on Isa. 48:18

Spiritual
Arr. by Lyndell Leatherman

1. I've got peace like a riv-er, I've got peace like a
2. I've got love like an o-cean, I've got love like an
3. I've got joy like a foun-tain, I've got joy like a

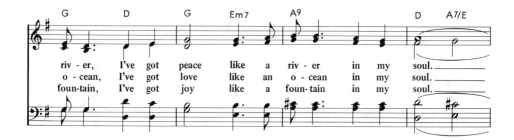

riv-er, I've got peace like a riv-er in my soul.
o-cean, I've got love like an o-cean in my soul.
foun-tain, I've got joy like a foun-tain in my soul.

I've got peace like a riv-er, I've got peace like a
I've got love like an o-cean, I've got love like an
I've got joy like a foun-tain, I've got joy like a

riv-er, I've got peace like a riv-er in my soul.
o-cean, I've got love like an o-dean, in my soul.
foun-tain, I've got joy like a foun-tain, in my soul.

JEREMIAH 29:13

109

(And Ye Shall Seek Me)

Robert Rhodes

110 JEREMIAH 31:12

Adapted by Ray Rempt

The Ash Grove
English folk tune
Arr., Roger Nachtwey

There - fore___ they shall come___ and sing in the height of Zi - on and shall flow to - geth - er to the good - ness of the Lord. *For wheat and for wine, for oil and for the young,___ for the young___ of the flock___ and of ___ the herd. And their soul shall be___ as a wa - tered gar - den, and they shall not sor - row an - y more___ at all.

* The melody may be sung as a canon, the second part entering at this point, in such case, omit the accompaniment second

JESUS FED 5000

St. 1, K. E.
St. 2-5, Henry Ehlen

Kathy Ehlen

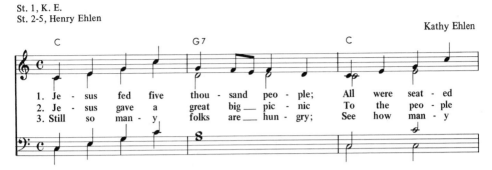

1. Je - sus fed five thou - sand peo - ple; All were seat - ed
2. Je - sus gave a great big __ pic - nic To the peo - ple
3. Still so man - y folks are __ hun - gry; See how man - y

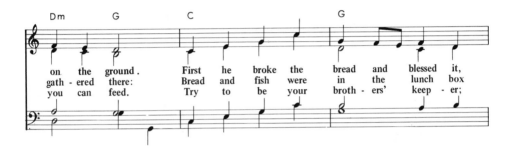

on the ground. First he broke the bread and blessed it,
gath - ered there: Bread and fish were in the lunch box
you can feed. Try to be your broth - ers' keep - er;

Then he passed it all a - round, Five loaves of
That a lit - tle boy did share, Five loaves of
Share your bread with those in need. Five loaves of

bread and two lit - tle fish.
bread and two lit - tle fish.
bread and two lit - tle fish.

112 FATHER WELCOMES

Smoothly

Fa - ther wel-comes all _ his chil- dren to _ his fam-'ly through his Son. _

Fa-ther giv-ing his _ sal - va - tion, Life _ for ev-er has been won.

won. 1. Lit - tle child - ren, come _ to me, for my king - dom is of these.
2. In the wa - ter, in _ the Word, in his prom - ise, be as - sured:
3. Let us dai - ly die _ to sin; let us dai - ly rise with him

Life and _ love I have to _ give, Mer - cy _ for your sin.
Those who are bap - tized and be - lieves, Shall be _ born a - gain.
Walk in the love of Christ our _ Lord, Live in the peace of God.

JESUS, KEEP ME
NEAR THE CROSS

113

Fanny J. Crosby

William Howard Doane

1. Je - sus, keep me near the Cross, There a pre - cious foun - tain
2. Near the Cross, a trembl - ing soul, Love and mer - cy found me;
3. Near the Cross! O Lamb of God, Bring its scen - es before me;
4. Near the Cross I'll watch and wait, Hop ing, trust - ing, ev - er,

Free to all a heal - ing stream, Flows from Cal - v'ry's moun - tain.
There the bright and morn - ing star Shed its beams a - round me.
Help me walk from day to day, With its shad - ows o'er me.
Till I reach the gold - en strand, Just be - yond the riv - er.

Chorus

In the Cross, in the Cross, Be my glo - ry ev - er;

Till my rap - tured soul shall find Rest be - yond the riv - er.

114 JESUS LOVES ME

Anna B. Warner, alt.

Wm. B. Bradbury

1. Je - sus loves me! This I know, for the Bi - ble tells me so:
2. Je - sus loves me! Loves me still, Tho' I'm ver - y weak and ill;
3. Je - sus loves me! He who died, Heav - en's gate to o - pen wide;
4. Je - sus loves me! He will stay Close be - side me all the way;

Lit - tle ones to Him be - long; They are weak but He is strong.
That I might from sin be free, Bled and died up - on the tree.
He will wash a - way my sin, Let His lit - tle child come in.
Thou hast bled and died for me, I will hence - forth live for thee.

Yes, Je - sus loves me! Yes, Je - sus loves me!

Yes, Je - sus loves me! The Bi - ble tells me so.

JESUS, NAME ABOVE ALL NAMES

115

Adapted by Naida Hearn from
Matt. 1:23; Phil. 2:5-11

Patricia Cain

1. Je - sus, name a - bove all names, beau - ti - ful Sav - ior, glo - ri - ous Lord, _____ Em - man - u - el, God is with us, bless - ed Re - deem - er, liv - ing Word.

2. Jesus, loving shepherd
   Vine of the branches, Son of God
   Prince of Peace, Wonderful counselor
   Lord of the universe, Light of the world.

3. Jesus, Way of salvation,
   King of kings, Lord of Lords,
   the way the truth, and the Life,
   Mighty creator, my Savior and friend.

116   JESUS, THOU ART HOLY

Unknown

1. Je - sus, Thou art ho - ly, the ho - ly Son of God, The ho - ly Son of God, The ho - ly Son of God; Al - le - lu - ia to Thy name, Al - le - lu - ia to Thy name, Al - le - lu - ia to Thy name, Je - sus.

2. Jesus, thou art worthy, worthy to be praised . . .

3. Jesus, thou art Savior, Savior of the world

4. Jesus, thou art master, master of my heart . . .

PEOPLE NEED THE LORD 117

Greg Nelson and Phill McHugh
Arr. by Henry Wiens

JOYFUL, JOYFUL, WE ADORE THEE

Henry Van Dyke

Arr. from Ludwig van Beethoven

118

1. Joy - ful, joy - ful, we a - dore Thee, God of glo - ry, Lord of love;
2. All Thy works with joy sur round Thee, Earth and heav'n re - flect Thy rays,
3. Thou art giv - ing and for - giv - ing, Ev - er bless - ing, ev - er blest,
4. Mor - tals, join the might - y cho - rus Which the morn - ing stars be - gan;

Hearts un - fold like flow'rs be - fore Thee, Hail Thee as the sun a - bove.
Stars and an - gels sing a - round Thee, Cen - ter of un - bro - ken praise;
Well - spring of the joy of liv - ing, O - cean - depth of hap - py rest!
Fa - ther love is reign - ing o'er us, Broth - er - love binds man to man.

Melt the clouds of sin and sad - ness; Drive the dark of doubt a - way;
Field and for - est, vale and moun - tain, Flow - 'ry mead - ow flash - ing sea,
Thou our Fa - ther, Christ our Broth - er, All who live in love are Thine:
Ev - er sing - ing, march we on - ward, Vic - tors in the midst of strife;

Giv - er of im - mor - tal glad - ness, Fill us with the light of day!
Chant - ing bird and flow - ing foun - tain, Call us to re - joice in Thee.
Teach us how to love each oth - er, Lift us to the Joy Di - vine.
Joy - ful mu - sic lifts us sun - ward In the tri - umph song of life.

119 JUST AS I AM

Charlotte Elliott

Wm. B. Bradbury

1. Just____ as I am,____ with - out____ one plea, But

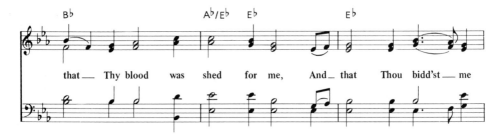

that ___ Thy blood was shed for me, And_ that Thou bidd'st ___ me

come to Thee,__ O Lamb of God, __ I come! I come!____

2. Just as I am, and waiting not,
   To rid my soul of one dark blot,
   To Thee whose blood can cleanse each spot,
   O Lamb of God, I come! I come!

3. Just as I am, tho' tossed about
   With many a conflict, many a doubt,
   Fightings and fears within, without,
   O Lamb of God, I come! I come!

4. Just as I am, poor, wretched, blind;
   Sight, riches, healing of the mind,
   Yea, all I need, in Thee to find,
   O Lamb of God, I come! I come!

5. Just as I am, Thou wilt receive,
   Wilt welcome, pardon, cleanse, relieve;
   Because Thy promise I believe,
   O Lamb of God, I come! I come!

LEAD ON, O KING ETERNAL 120

Ernest W. Schurtleff

Henry Smart

1. Lead on, O King E - ter - nal, The day of march has come; Hence forth in fields of con - quest Thy tents shall be our home. Thro' days of prep - a - ra - tion Thy grace has made us strong, And now, O King E - ter - nal, We lift our bat - tle song.

2. Lead on, O King E - ter - nal, Till sin's fierce war shall cease, And ho - li - ness shall whis - per The sweet A - men of peace; For not with swords loud clash - ing, Nor roll of stir - ring drums; With deeds of love and mer - cy, The heaven - ly king - dom comes.

3. Lead on, O King E - ter - nal, We fol - low, not with fears; For glad - ness breaks like morn - ing Where - 'er Thy face ap - pears; Thy cross is lift - ed o'er us; We jour - ney in its light: The crown a - waits the con - quest; Lead on, O God of might.

121 LET ALL THAT IS WITHIN ME

Adapted from Ps. 103:1; Rev. 5:12

Unknown
Arr. by Lyndell Leatherman

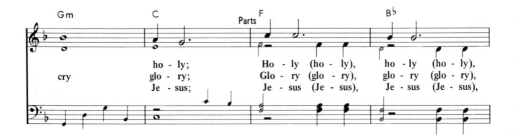

LET OUR PRAISE TO YOU
BE AS INCENSE

Words and Music by
Brent Chambers

join the hosts of an - gels, and pro - claim to - geth - er Your

ho - li - ness. _____ **1.** Let our ___ **2.** Ho - ly, ho - ly,

ho - ly, ho - ly is the Lord.

repeat several times

123 FOR GOD SO LOVED THE WORLD

Frances Townsend

Alfred B. Smith

1. For God so loved the world He gave His on - ly Son To
2. Some day He's com - ing back What glo - ry that will

die on Cal -v'ry's tree, From sin to set me free;

be! Won - der - ful His love to me. _____

LET THE HILLS
NOW SING FOR JOY

Ps. 98

Gary Johnson

2nd Part (optional)

O, let the hills

Melody

1. O let the hills now sing for
2. Sing to the Lord a brand new
3. Break forth in joy with hap - py

now sing for joy! And let the

joy! And let the sea
song! For He has done
song! Praise to the Lord

sea now roar its praise!

___ now roar its praise! And let the
___ glo - ri - ous deeds! His own right
___ in sym - pho - 'ny! Let all the

LET THE WORDS
OF MY MOUTH

125

Psalm 19:14

John Worre

Let the words of my mouth, and the
med-i-ta-tions of my heart, be ac-cep-ta-ble in Thy sight,
oh Lord, oh Lord, Let the
(Lord) oh Lord, my strength, and my re -
deem - - er. oh (er).

126 LET US BREAK BREAD TOGETHER

Traditional Spiritual

2. Let us drink wine (or the cup) together . . .   3. Let us bow 'round the alter . . .
4. Let us praise God together . . . .

LET US PRAY

127

Words and Music by
Ray Hildebrand

Let us pray un-to the Lord in u-ni-ty and one ac-cord. Take the hand of the one stand-ing by your side, And let's con-fess un-to the Lord that we have failed and fal-len short; And He will hear us, ___ and He will help us. ___ Let us pray. ___

128 LET'S JUST PRAISE THE LORD

William J. and Gloria Gaither

William J. Gaither

Let's just praise _____ the Lord!
praise _____ the Lord! Let's just lift our hearts to
heav - en and praise the Lord;
lift our hearts to heav - en and praise the Lord! _____

John 12:32

Unknown

1. Let's lift up Je - sus.____ Let's lift up Je - sus.____

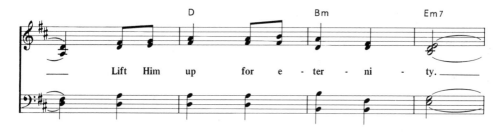

____ Lift Him up for e - ter - ni - ty.____

____ He said, "If I ____ be lift - ed up from the

earth, I will draw all men un - to me."

2. Let's lift Him higher. Let's lift Him higher.
Lift Him up for eternity.
He said, "If I be lifted up from the earth,
I will draw all men unto me."

130 LIFT HIGH THE CROSS

George W. Kitchin, Michael R. Newbolt

Sydney H. Nicholson

1. Come Christians, follow where our captain trod, Our king victorious, Christ, the Son of God.
2. Led on their way by this triumphant sign, The hosts of God in conqu'ring ranks combine.
3. All new-born soldiers of the Crucified, Bear on their brows the seal of him who died.
4. O Lord, once lifted on the glorious tree, As thou hast promised, draw us all to thee.

5. So shall our song of triumph ever be:
   Praise to the Crucified for victory! Refrain

LIFT UP YOUR HEADS, OH YE GATES

131

Psalm 24

Public Domain

Lift up your heads, oh ye gates, and be lift-ed up, ye ev-er-last-ing doors. And the King of glo-ry shall come in. The King of glo-ry shall come in. Who is this King of glo-ry? Who is this King of glo-ry? The Lord, the strong and might-y, The Lord might-y in bat-tle.

132 LORD, SPEAK TO ME THAT I MAY SPEAK

Frances R. Havergal

Robert Schumann

1. Lord, speak to me, that I may speak
2. O lead me, Lord, that I may lead
3. O teach me, Lord, that I may teach
4. O fill me, with Thy ful - ness, Lord,

In liv - ing ech - oes of Thy tone;
The wan - d'ring and the wav - 'ring feet;
The pre - cious things Thou dost im - part;
Un - til my ver - y heart o'er - flow

As Thou hast sought, so let me seek
O feed me, Lord, that I may feed
And wing my words, that they may reach
In kind - ling thought and glow - ing word,

Thy err - ing chil - dren lost and lone.
Thy hun - g'ring ones with man - na sweet.
Thy hid - den depths of many a heart.
Thy love to tell, Thy praise to show.

LOVE, LOVE

Arr. Roger Nachtwey

Round: Successive voices enter after each two measures.

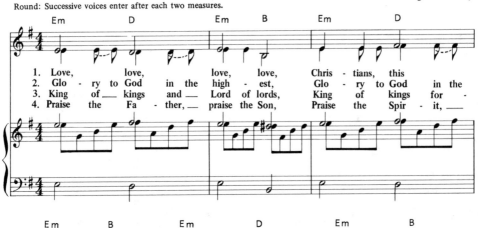

1. Love, love, love, love, Chris - tians, this
2. Glo - ry to God in the high - est, Glo - ry to God in the
3. King of kings and Lord of lords, King of kings for -
4. Praise the Fa - ther, praise the Son, Praise the Spir - it,

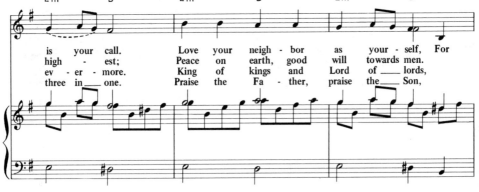

is your call. Love your neigh - bor as your - self, For
high - est; Peace on earth, good will towards men.
ev - er - more. King of kings and Lord of lords,
three in one. Praise the Fa - ther, praise the Son,

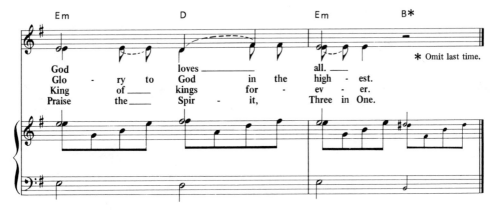

God loves all.
Glo - ry to God in the high - est.
King of kings for - ev - er.
Praise the Spir - it, Three in One.

* Omit last time.

134 # LOVE, LOVE, LOVE

Herbert Brokering

Lois Brokering

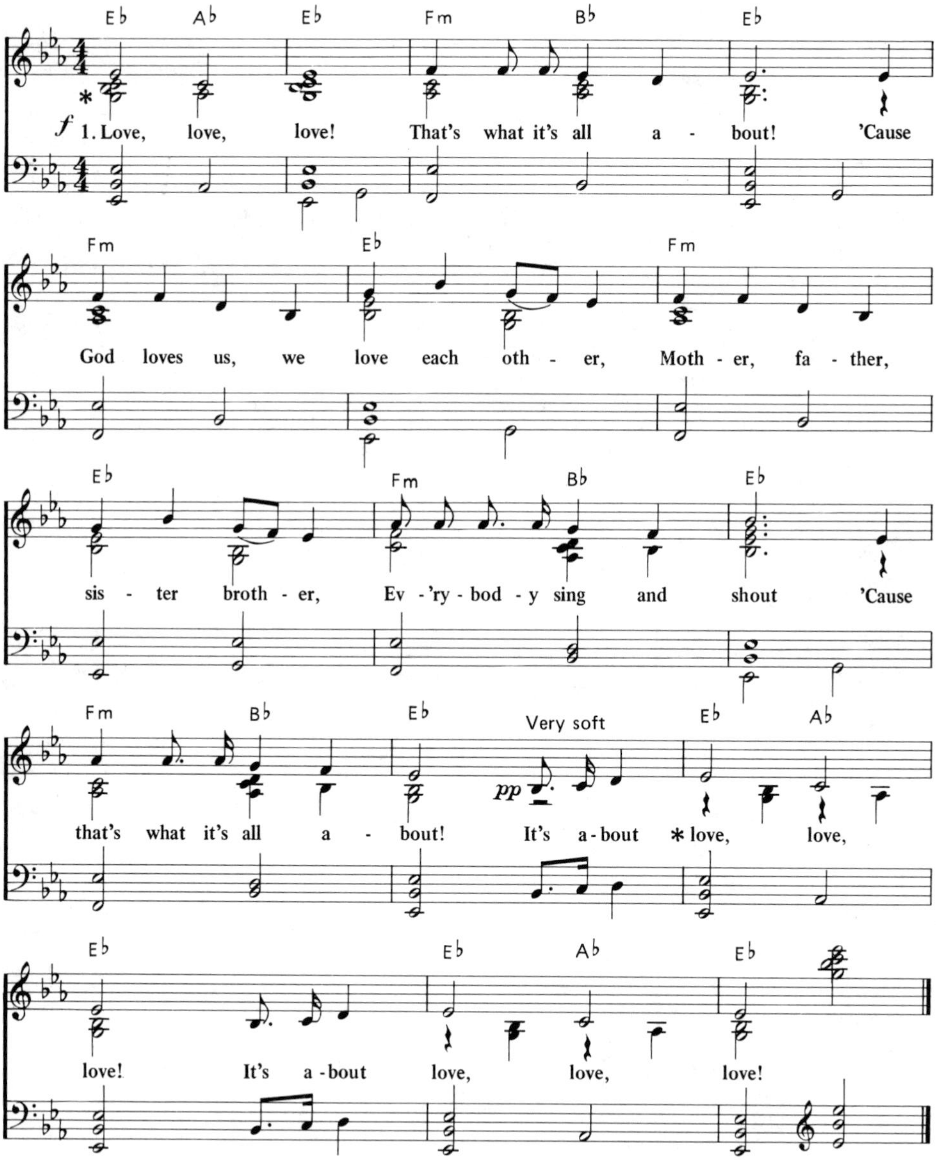

Lyrics:
f 1. Love, love, love! That's what it's all a - bout! 'Cause
God loves us, we love each oth - er, Moth - er, fa - ther,
sis - ter broth - er, Ev - 'ry - bod - y sing and shout 'Cause
that's what it's all a - bout! It's a - bout *love, love,
love! It's a - bout love, love, love!

* 2; Peace, peace, peace!   3. Joy, joy, joy!
  4. Me, me, me!   5. You, you, you!

MAJESTY

135

Words and Music by
Jack Hayford

alt, lift up on high the name of Je - sus. _____ Mag - ni -

fy. Come glo - ri - fy Christ Je - sus the King. _____

D.S. al Fine

136   WORTHY IS THE LAMB

Words and Music by
Don Wyrtzen

Wor - thy is the Lamb that was slain, _____ Wor - thy is the

Lamb that was slain, _____ Wor - thy is the Lamb that was slain, _____

137 MAKE ME A CAPTIVE, LORD

George Matheson

George William Martin
Arr. Arthur S. Sullivan

In moderate time

1. Make me a captive, Lord, And then I shall be free;
2. My heart is weak and poor Until it master find;

Force me to render up my sword, And I shall conqueror be.
It has no spring of action sure, It varies with the wind.

I sink in life's alarms When by myself I stand;
It cannot freely move Till thou hast wrought its chain;

Imprison me within thine arms, And strong shall be my hand.
Enslave it with thy matchless love, And deathless it shall reign. A-men.

3. My power is faint and low
   Till I have learned to serve;
   It wants the needed fire to glow,
   It wants the breeze to nerve;
   It cannot drive the world
   Until itself be driven;
   Its flag can only be unfurled
   When thou shalt breathe from heaven.

4. My will is not my own
   Til thou hast made it thine;
   If it would reach a monarch's throne
   It must its crown resign;
   It only stands unbent
   Amid the clashing strife,
   When on thy bosom it has leant
   And found in thee its life. Amen.

MAKE ME LIKE YOU

138

Words and Music by
Jimmy and Carol Owens

139 MY FAITH LOOKS UP TO THEE

Ray Palmer

Lowell Mason

1. My faith looks up to Thee, Thou Lamb of Cal - va - ry, Sav - iour di - vine! Now hear me while I pray, Take all my guilt a - way, O let me from this day Be whol - ly Thine!

2. May Thy rich grace im - part strength to my faint - ing heart My zeal in - spire; As Thou hast died for me, O may my love to Thee Pure, warm and change - less be, A liv - ing fire!

3. While life's dark maze I tread, And griefs a - round me spread Be Thou my guide; Bid dark - ness turn to day, Wipe sor - row's tears a - way, Nor let me ev - er stray From Thee a - side.

4. When ends life's tran - sient dream, When death's cold, sul - len stream Shall o'er me roll; Blest Sav - iour, then, in love, Fear and dis - trust re - move; O bear me safe a - bove, A ran - somed soul!

MAKE THIS CHILD YOURS 140

Words and Music by
Gloria Lien

Take this child, Make her yours, Make her part of your fam - i - ly. From your
(him) (him)

love she has come; In your love may she al - ways be. Let not
(he) (he)

time or age take her far from your fam - i - ly. May she
(him) (he)

grow; may she stay close to you. To
(he)

little faster

you, _____ dear Lord, we praise thee _____ for the

bless - ings of your perfect gift _____ To

you, _____ dear Lord, our heart - felt thanks, we lift our

voice in praise. _____ Take this

Coda

you.

D.S.

MARY'S LITTLE BOY CHILD 141

Words and Music by
Jester Hairston

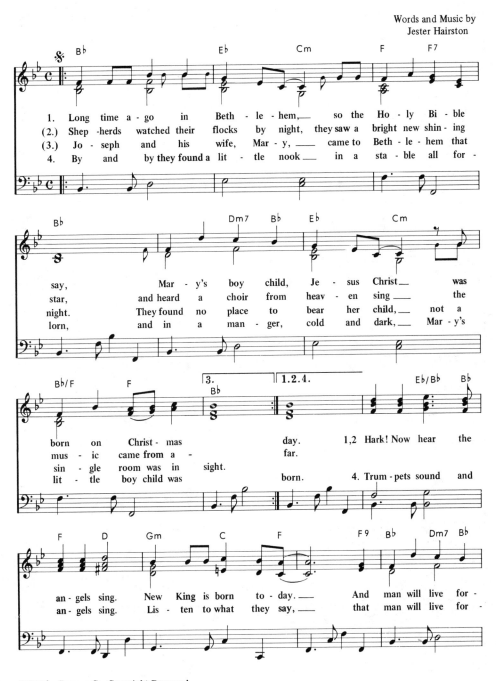

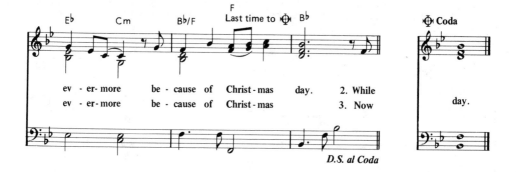

ev - er - more be - cause of Christ - mas day. 2. While
ev - er - more be - cause of Christ - mas day. 3. Now

day.

D.S. al Coda

142 WE WILL GLORIFY

Twila Paris
Arr. Henry Wiens

1. We will glo - ri - fy the King of Kings; We will
2. Hal - le - lu - jah to the King of Kings; Hal - le -
3. Lord Je - ho - vah reigns in maj - es - ty; We will

glo - ri - fy the Lamb; We will glo - ri - fy the
lu - jah to the Lamb; Hal - le - lu - jah to the
bow be - fore His throne; We will wor - ship Him in

Lord of Lords, Who ___ is the great I Am.
Lord of Lords, Who ___ is the great I Am.
right - eous - ness; We will wor - ship Him a - lone.

MY FAITH STILL HOLDS

143

William J. and Gloria Gaither

William J. Gaither

144 MY JESUS, I LOVE THEE

Anonynous

Adoniram J. Gordon

1. My Jesus, I love Thee, I know Thou art mine,
2. I love Thee because Thou hast first loved me,
3. I'll love Thee in life, I will love Thee in death,
4. In mansions of glory and endless delight,

For Thee all the follies of sin I resign;
And purchased my pardon on Calvary's tree;
And praise Thee as long as Thou lendest me breath;
I'll ever adore Thee in heaven so bright;

My gracious Redeemer, my Savior art Thou,
I love Thee for wearing the thorns on Thy brow,
And say when the death-dew lies cold on my brow,
I'll sing with the glittering crown on my brow,

If ever I loved Thee, my Jesus, 'tis now.
If ever I loved Thee, my Jesus, 'tis now.
If ever I loved Thee, my Jesus, 'tis now.
If ever I loved Thee, my Jesus, 'tis now.

MY TRIBUTE

145

Words & Music by
Andrae Crouch

To God, be the glo - ry, to God, be the glo - ry, To

God be the glo - ry, for the things He has done! With His

blood He has saved me, With His pow'r He has raised me; To

God be the glo - ry, For the things___ He has done! done. Just let me

Fine

live   my   life,   Let it be pleas-ing Lord, to Thee;   And if I

gain   an-y praise,   Let it go to Cal - va - ry!   With His

D.S.

146   LORD, WE PRAISE YOU

Otis Skillings

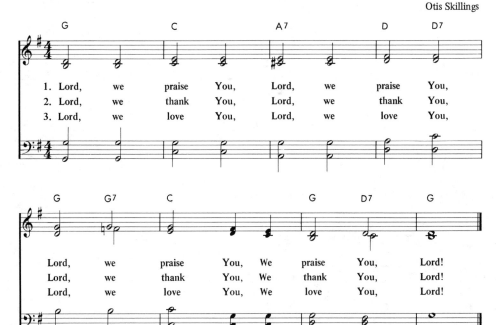

1. Lord,   we   praise   You,   Lord,   we   praise   You,
2. Lord,   we   thank   You,   Lord,   we   thank   You,
3. Lord,   we   love   You,   Lord,   we   love   You,

Lord,   we   praise   You,   We   praise   You,   Lord!
Lord,   we   thank   You,   We   thank   You,   Lord!
Lord,   we   love   You,   We   love   You,   Lord!

NEW TESTAMENT SONG 147

Source Unknown

Mat - thew, Mark and Luke and John, Acts, Ro - mans, First and Sec - ond Cor - in - thi - ans, Ga - la - tians, E - phe - sians, Phil - ip - pi - ans, Col - os - sians, First and Sec - ond Thes - sa - lo - ni - ans, First Tim - o - thy, Sec - ond Tim - o - thy, Ti - tus, Phi - le - mon, He - brews, James, ___ First Pe - ter Sec - ond Pe - ter, three Johns, Jude and Re - vel - a - tion.

148 O LOVE THAT WILT NOT LET ME GO

George Matheson

Albert L. Peace

1. O Love that wilt not let me go, I rest my wea-ry soul in Thee; I give Thee back the life I owe, That in Thine o-cean depths its flow May rich-er, full-er be.

2. O Light that fol-l'west all my way, I yield my flick-'ring torch to Thee; My heart re-stores its bor-rowed ray, That in Thy sun-shine's blaze its day May bright-er, fair-er be.

3. O Joy that seek-est me thro' pain, I can-not close my heart to Thee: I trace the rain-bow thro' the rain, And feel the prom-ise is not vain, That morn shall tear-less be.

4. O Cross that lift-est up my head, I dare not ask to fly from Thee; I lay in dust life's glo-ry dead, And from the ground there blos-soms red Life that shall end-less be.

NO ONE EVER CARED FOR ME LIKE JESUS

149

Words and Music by
C. F. Weigle

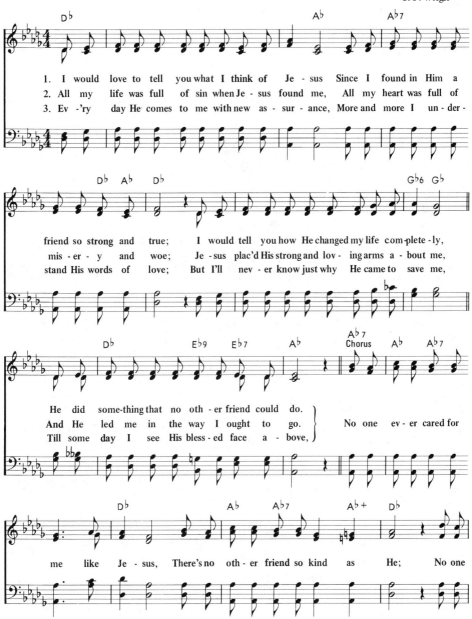

1. I would love to tell you what I think of Je-sus Since I found in Him a
2. All my life was full of sin when Je-sus found me, All my heart was full of
3. Ev-'ry day He comes to me with new as-sur-ance, More and more I un-der-

friend so strong and true; I would tell you how He changed my life com-plete-ly,
mis-er-y and woe; Je-sus plac'd His strong and lov-ing arms a-bout me,
stand His words of love; But I'll nev-er know just why He came to save me,

He did some-thing that no oth-er friend could do.
And He led me in the way I ought to go.
Till some day I see His bless-ed face a-bove,

No one ev-er cared for
me like Je-sus, There's no oth-er friend so kind as He; No one

else could take the sin and dark-ness from me, O how much He cared for me.

150 I HAVE THE JOY

Arr. by H. D. L.

1. I have the joy, joy, joy, joy, down in my heart,
2. I have the peace that pass-es un-der-stand-ing, down in my heart,
3. I have the love of Je-sus, love of Je-sus, down in my heart,

*
Down in my heart, down in my heart; I have the joy, joy,
Down in my heart, down in my heart; I have the peace that pass-es
Down in my heart, down in my heart; I have the love of Je-sus,

*
joy, joy, down in my heart, Down in my heart to stay.
un-der-stand-ing, down in my heart, Down in my heart to stay.
love of Je-sus, down in my heart, Down in my heart to stay.

* "Where!"

OH, FOR A THOUSAND TONGUES

Charles Wesley

William Gardiner

151

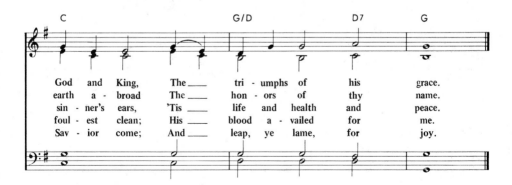

1. Oh, for a thou - sand tongues to sing My great Re - deem - er's praise, The tri - umphs of his grace.
2. My, gra - cious Mas - ter and my God, As - sist me to pro - claim, To spread through all the earth a - broad The hon - ors of thy name.
3. Je - sus, the name that charms our fears, That bids our sor - rows cease, Tis mu - sic in the sin - ner's ears, 'Tis life and health and peace.
4. He breaks the pow'r of can - celed sin, He sets the pris - 'ner free, His blood can make the foul - est clean; His blood a - vailed for me.
5. Hear him, ye deaf; his praise, ye dumb, Your loos - ened tongues em - ploy; Ye blind, be - hold your Sav - ior come; And leap, ye lame, for joy.

152   OH, HOW I LOVE JESUS

Words and Music by
Frederick Whitfield

1. Oh, how I love Je - sus,
Oh, how I love Je - sus.
Oh, how I love Je - sus, Be -
cause He first loved me.

2. To me, He is so wonderful (3 times)
   Because He first loved me.

3. And now, He is my righteousness (3 times)
   Because He first loved me.

OH, HOW HE LOVES
YOU AND ME

Adapted from John 15:13; I John 4:9-10

153

Kurt Kaiser

154 OPEN MINE EYES

Clarence A. Johnson

ON EAGLE'S WINGS

155

Words and Music by
Michael Joncas

1. You who dwell in the shel-ter of the Lord, who a-bide in His sha-dow for life
2. Snare of the fowl-er will nev-er cap-ture you, and fa-mine will bring you no fear
3. You need not fear the terr-or of the night, not the ar-row that flies by day;

Say to the Lord, "My re-fuge, my
un-der His wings your re-fuge, His
though thou-sands fall a-bout you,

Rock in whom I trust.
faith-ful-ness your shield.
near, you it shall not come.

And He will raise you up on

ea-gle wings bear you on the breath of dawn, make you to shine like the

sun, and hold you in the palm of His hand. 2. The

Fine

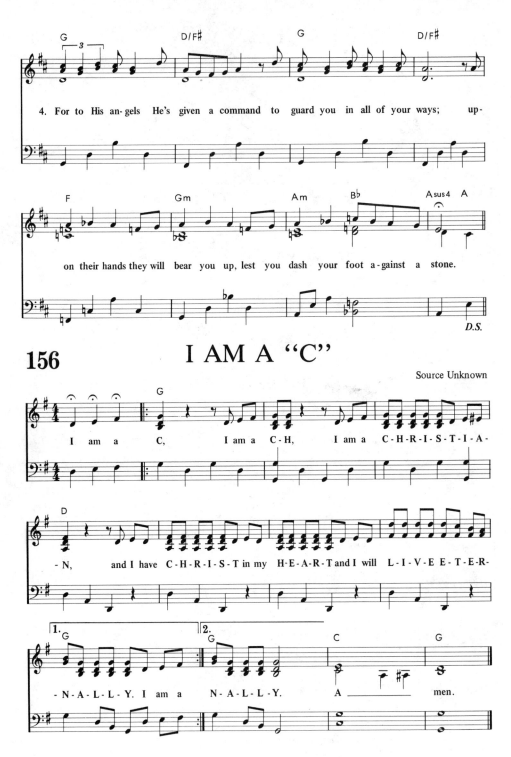

4. For to His an-gels He's given a command to guard you in all of your ways; up-on their hands they will bear you up, lest you dash your foot a-gainst a stone.

D.S.

156

I AM A "C"

Source Unknown

I am a   C,   I am a   C-H,   I am a   C-H-R-I-S-T-I-A--N,   and I have C-H-R-I-S-T in my H-E-A-R-T and I will L-I-V-E E-T-E-R--N-A-L-L-Y. I am a   N-A-L-L-Y.   A _____ men.

OPEN OUR EYES

157

Words & Music by
Bob Cull

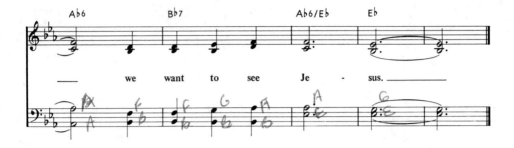

we want to see Je - sus.

158

I LOVE YOU, LORD

Words & Music by
John Worre

I love You, Lord, I love

You. You're the source of all that's

good and I love You.

OPEN MY EYES,
THAT I MAY SEE

159

Words and Music by
Chas. H. Scott

1. O-pen my eyes, that I may see Glimps-es of truth Thou hast for me;
2. O-pen my ears, that I may hear Voi-ces of truth Thou send-est clear;
3. O-pen my mouth, and let me bear Glad-ly the warm truth ev-'ry-where;

Place in my hands the won-der-ful key That shall un-clasp, and set me free.
And while the wave-notes fall on my ear, Ev-'ry-thing false will dis-ap-pear.
O-pen my heart, and let me pre-pare Love with Thy chil-dren thus to share.

Si-lent-ly now I wait for Thee, Read-y, my God, Thy will to see;
Si-lent-ly now I wait for Thee, Read-y, my God, Thy will to see;
Si-lent-ly now I wait for Thee, Read-y, my God, Thy will to see;

O-pen my eyes, il-lu-mine me, Spir-it di-vine!
O-pen my ears, il-lu-mine me, Spir-it di-vine!
O-pen my heart, il-lu-mine me, Spir-it di-vine!

160 PASSED THRU THE WATERS

Words and Music by
Richard Avery
Donald Marsh

OUR GOD REIGNS

161

Isaiah 52:7,53

Words & Music by Leonard E. Smith, Jr.

Capo 1, Play A

1. How love-ly on the moun-tains are the feet of Him
2. He had no state - ly form, He had no maj - es - ty,
3. It was our sin and guilt that bruised and wound - ed Him.
4. Meek as a lamb that's led out to the slaugh - ter house,
5. Out from the tomb He came with grace and ma - je - sty,

who brings good news, good news,
that we should be drawn to Him.
It was our sin that brought Him down.
Dumb as a sheep before its shearer,
He is al - ive, He is alive.

an - nounc - ing peace, pro - claim - ing news of hap - pi - ness
He was des - pised and we took no ac - count of Him,
When we like sheep had gone a - stray, our shep - herd came
His life ran down up on the ground like pour - ing rain,
God loves us so, see here His hands, His feet, His side,

OUR NEW SONG OF PRAISE 162

Adapted from Ps. 40

David Steele

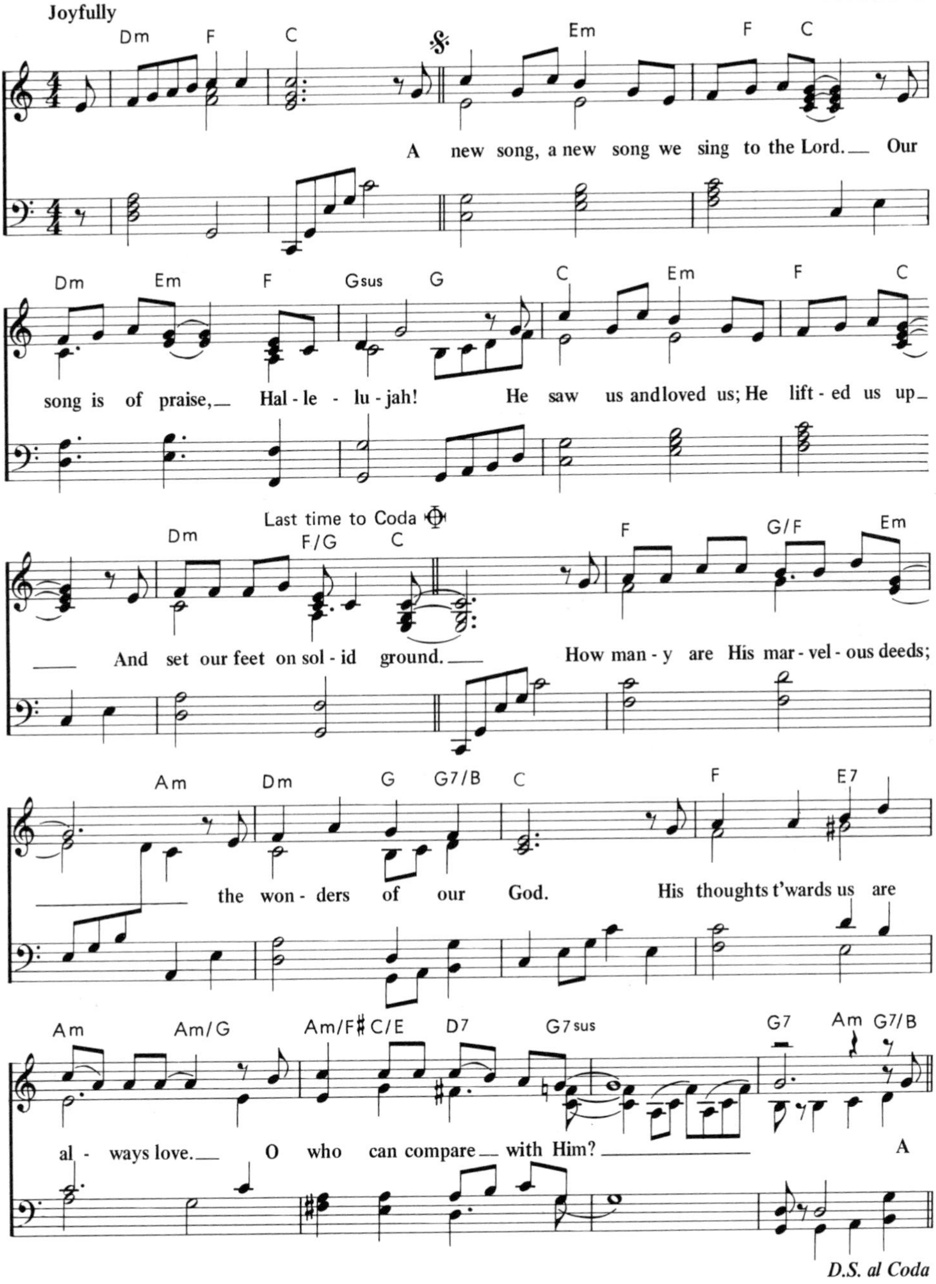
Joyfully
Dm F C Em F C
A new song, a new song we sing to the Lord. Our
Dm Em F Gsus G C Em F C
song is of praise, Hal-le-lu-jah! He saw us and loved us; He lift-ed us up
Last time to Coda
Dm F/G C F G/F Em
And set our feet on sol-id ground. How man-y are His mar-vel-ous deeds;
Am Dm G G7/B C F E7
the won-ders of our God. His thoughts t'wards us are
Am Am/G Am/F♯ C/E D7 G7sus G7 Am G7/B
al-ways love. O who can compare with Him? A
D.S. al Coda

Coda

Our song of praise we sing to God!

163
JESUS, PLEASE WATCH OVER US

With quiet dignity

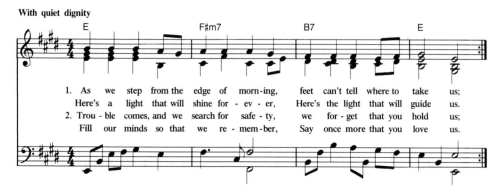

1. As we step from the edge of morn-ing, feet can't tell where to take us;
   Here's a light that will shine for - ev - er, Here's the light that will guide us.
2. Trou - ble comes, and we search for safe - ty, we for - get that you hold us;
   Fill our minds so that we re - mem-ber, Say once more that you love us.

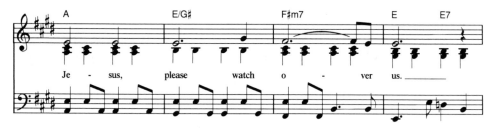

Je - sus, please watch o - ver us.

Je - sus, please take care of us.

3. Danger meets us at every moment,
   death is never in hiding;
   You are stronger than any danger,
   you are stronger than dying.

4. In your life is the Father's welcome,
   in your death there is freedom;
   Be our life and our death forever,
   Be our new resurrection.

PASS IT ON

164

Words & Music by
Kurt Kaiser

1. It on - ly takes a spark to get a fire going
2. won - drous time is spring when all the trees are bud - ding
3. wish for you my friend this hap - pi - ness that I've found

And soon all those a - round can warm up in its
The birds be - gin to sing; The flow - ers, start their
You can de - pend on Him, It mat - ters not where

glow - ing That's how it is with God's love
bloom - ing That's how it is with God's love
you're bound I'll shout it from the moun - tain top

Once you've ex - pe - ri-enced it you spread His love to ev - 'ry - one; You
Once you've ex - pe - ri-enced it you want to sing it's fresh like spring; You
I want my world to know; The Lord of love has come to me, I

want to pass it on. _____ 2. What a _____

want to pass it on. _____ 3. I __ _____

want to pass it on. _____ I'll

shout it from the moun-tain top I want my world to know,_ The

Lord of love has come to me, I want to pass it on. _____

165   LET THE GLORY OF THE LORD ENDURE

Adapted from Ps. 104:31, 33

Words and Music by
Keith Chrysler

Let the glo-ry of the Lord en - dure for - ev - er. Let the

Lord be glad in His works. I will sing un - to the Lord. as

long as I live, I will sing praise to my God while I have my being.

May also be used as a round

PRAISE HIM

Words and Music by
Tom Elie

Praise Him, praise Him! He's the one that's wor - thy, He's the One who saves. Je - sus, Je - sus! Praise the name of the___ Lord!___

167 PRAISE HIM, PRAISE HIM

Anon.

Praise Him, praise Him, all ye lit - tle chil - dren;
God is love, God is love.

Praise Him, praise Him, all ye lit - tle chil - dren;
God is love, God is love.

2. Love Him,   3. Thank Him,   4. Serve Him,   5. Crown Him,

PRAISE THE LORD

168

Words by
Chuck Girard, Jay Truax
and Herb Brendlin

Music by
Tom Coomes and Fred Field

169 PRAISE THE LORD

Words and Music by
Brown Bannister
Mike Hudson

Praise the Lord, ____ He can work thru those who praise Him. Praise the

Lord, ____ for our God in-hab-its praise. Praise the Lord, ____ for the

chains that seem to bind you, serve on-ly to re-mind you that they drop

pow-er-less be-hind you when you praise ____ Him. ____

PRAISE TO THE FATHER   170

Elizabeth Charles

Friedrich F. Flemming, 1778-1813

1. Praise to the Father for His loving kindness: Tenderly cares He for His erring children; Praise Him, all angels, praise Him in the heavens, Praise to Jehovah.

2. Praise to the Savior, great is His compassion; Graciously cares He for His chosen people; Young men and women, aging folk and children, Praise to the Savior.

3. Praise to the Spirit, Comforter of Israel, Sent of the Father and the Son to bless us, Praise to the Father, Son, and Holy Spirit, Praise to the Triune God.

171 PRAISE YOU, FATHER

Words and Music by
Jim Stipech

Praise —— you, Fa - ther, —— bless —— you, Je - sus. ——

Ho - ly Spir - it, thank you for be - ing here, —— be -ing here. __

Praise—— you, Fa - ther,—— bless—— you, Je -sus, —— Ho - ly Spir - it,

thank you for be-ing here,—— be-ing here —— Lord. _____

PRAISE TO THE LORD

172

Joachim Neander
Tr. Catherine Winkworth

Stralsund Gesangbuch, 1665
Arr. Roger Nachtwey

1. Praise to the Lord, the Al - might - y, the King of cre - a - tion;
O my soul, praise him, for he is thy health and sal - va - tion:
All ye who hear, Now to his tem - ple draw near; Join - ing in

2. Praise to the Lord, who o'er all things so won - drous - ly
reign - eth, Shel - ters thee un - der his wings, yea, so gent - ly
sus - tain - eth: Hast thou not seen? All that is need - ful hath
been Grant - ed in

3. Praise to the Lord, who doth pros - per thy work and de -
fend thee; Sure - ly his good - ness and mer - cy here dai - ly
at - tend thee. Pon - der a - new What the Al - might - y can
do, If with his

4. Praise to the Lord, O let all that is in me a -
dore him; All that hath life and breath, come now with prais - es
be - fore him! Let the A - men Sound from his peo - ple a -
gain; Glad - ly for

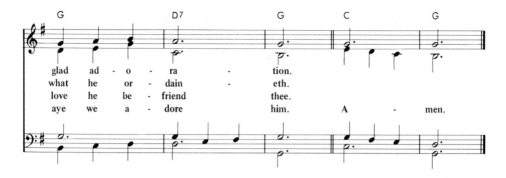

glad ad - o - ra - tion.
what he or - dain - eth.
love he be - friend thee.
aye we a - dore him. A - men.

173 PRAISE THE NAME OF JESUS

Words and Music by
Roy Hicks

Praise the name of Je - sus praise the name of Je - sus

He's my rock He's my fort - ress He's my de - liv - er - er in

him will I trust praise the name of Je - sus

PRAYER OF ST. FRANCIS 174

Adapted by
Sebastian Temple

Music by Sebastian Temple
Arranged by Betty Carr Pulkingham

joy._____ Oh, Mas-ter, grant that I may nev-er

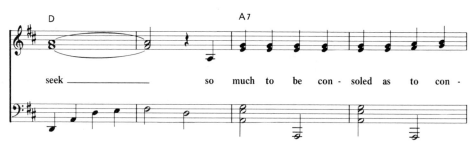

seek _____ so much to be con-soled as to con-

sole, _____ to be un-der-stood as to un-der-

stand, _____ to be loved as to love with all my

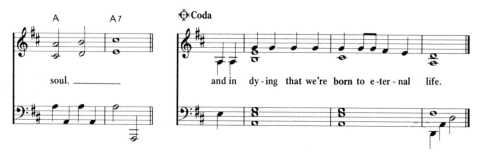

soul. _____

and in dy-ing that we're born to e-ter-nal life.

Ewald Bash

Traditional American melody

1. O____ Lord,__ our Lord, how ma - jes - tic your name is! How
2. When I think of the heav - ens, the work of your fin - gers, The
3. You__ made him, Lord in your own im - age and like - ness, And

great is your name__ in all __ the earth!_____ Your
moon and the stars you have set far in space, _____ What is
crowned him with hon - or and glo - ry; _____ You __

glo - ry is chant - ed a - bove the high heav - ens, You
man in your mem - 'ry a man that you're mind - ful, The
gave him do - min - ion o'er all of the wide earth, And

still all your foes through a child in his birth. _____
son _____ of man that you're car - ing for him. _____
o - ver the crea - tures that pass through the sea. _____

repeat stanza 1

176 RAISED FROM DEATH TO LOVE AND LIVING

Words and Music by
Paul Sweetwater

1. Raised from death to love and liv - ing,
2. What a lov - ing, faith - ful fa - ther,
3. God, who knows our thoughts and act - ions,
4. God, who planned and gave and suf - fered,

Freed from sin to serve our Lord;
Might - y God; who knows each need.
Soon will judge us by His Son.
Took our pain and death and sin.

Called to share His hol - y pur - pose,
All His paths are truth and kind - ness.
Each will then ap - pear be - fore Him.
What a price to buy a sin - ner.

Know His like - ness here re - stored;
When we dai - ly let Him lead.
See His per - fect jus - tice done.
Where can grat - i - tude be - gin?

177 REST IN HIS LOVE AND ABIDE

Based on Romans 15:13
Paul Johnson

Bob Krogstad

May the God of hope touch you with His love As you place your trust in His Son; May His gen-tle Spir-it fill you with His joy As you walk by faith in what He's done. May His peace fol-low you in be-liev-ing As you find sweet re-lease in re-ceiv-ing;

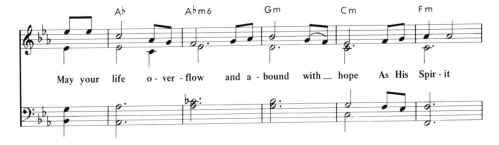

May your life o-ver-flow and a-bound with _ hope As His Spir-it

fills you in - side; _____ May you know His pow'r ev - 'ry-

day of your life As you trust in Him now to pro - vide. _____

_ Simp - ly rest in His love and a - bide, _____

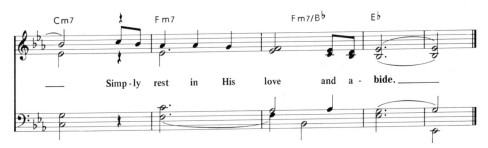

_ Simp - ly rest in His love and a - bide. _____

178

COME, HOLY SPIRIT

John W. Peterson
Arr. by Henry Wiens

J.W.P.

D   G   Em   A

1. The Ho-ly Spir-it came at Pen - te-cost,   He came in might-y full-ness
2. Then in an age when dark-ness gripped the earth,   "The just shall live by faith" was

D   A/C#   Bm   Bm/A   Em   A

then; _____ His wit-ness thru be-liev-ers won the lost,   And mul-ti-tudes were born a-
learned; _____ The Ho-ly Spir-it gave the Church new birth   As ref-or-ma-tion fires _

D   D   G

gain.   The ear-ly Chris-tians scat-tered o'er the world,
burned.   In la-ter years the great re - viv - als came,

Em   A   D   A/C#   Bm   Bm/A

They preached the gos-pel fear-less - ly; _____ Tho some were mar-tyred and to
When saints would seek the Lord and pray; _____ O once a-gain we need that

Em   A   A7   D

li - ons hurled,   They marched a-long in vic-to - ry!
ho - ly Flame   To meet the chall-enge of to - day!

Come, Ho - ly Spir - it, Dark is the hour, _____

We need Your fill - ing, Your love and Your might - y pow'r; _____

Move now a - mong us, Stir us, we pray, _____

Come, Ho - ly Spir - it, Re-vive the Church to - day!

Spir - it, Re-vive the Church to - day!

179 ROAD IN WINTER

Words and Music by
Reynolds W. Guyer
Arr. by Henry Wiens

The road in win-ter is bit-ter and win-dy, Two lone-ly peo-ple are tra-velled and worn; At last come to rest in a cold dus-ty sta-ble, There a child is born; There a child is born.

1. Here comes the sun climb-in' bright on the hill-side, sounds in the town call-in' out the new day; Clear from a sta-ble the cry of a ba-by; Be-

2. said a child would be born in the win-ter, Enter in si-lence make read-y His way; His moth-er is gen-tle, His fa-ther is quiet; Be-

3. Here comes the sun climb-in' bright on the hill-side, sounds in the town call-in' out the new day; Clear from a sta-ble the cry of a ba-by; Be-

180 REJOICE IN THE LORD ALWAYS

Philippians 4:4
Two Part Round

Words and Music by
Evelyn Tarner

ROCK OF AGES, CLEFT FOR ME

181

August M. Toplady

Thomas Hastings

1. Rock of A - ges, cleft for me, Let me
2. Not the la - bor of my hands Can ful -
3. Noth - ing in my hands I bring, Sim - ply
4. While I draw this fleet - ing breath, When my

hide my - self in Thee; Let the wa - ter and the blood,
fil Thy law's de - mands; Could my zeal no res - pite know,
to Thy cross I cling; Nak - ed, come to Thee for dress,
eyes shall close in death, When I soar to worlds un - known,

From Thy riv - en side which flowed, Be of
Could my tears for - ev - er flow, All for
Help - less look to Thee for grace; Foul, I
See Thee on Thy judg - ment - throne, Rock of

sin the doub - le cure, Save me from its guilt and pow'r.
sin could not a - tone; Thou must save, and Thou a - lone.
to the foun - tain fly, Wash me. Sav - ior, or I die.
A - ges, cleft for me, Let me hide my - self in Thee.

182 PROMISES

Terry K. Dittmer
Arr. by Henry Wiens

183 SAVIOR, LIKE A SHEPHERD LEAD US

Anonymous

William T. Bradbury

1. Sav - ior, like a shep-herd lead us, Much we need Thy ten - der care;
2. We are Thine, do Thou be - friend us, Be the Guar-dian of our way;
3. Thou hast prom-ised to re - ceive us, Poor and sin - ful though we be;
4. Ear - ly let us seek Thy fa - vor; Ear - ly let us do Thy will;

In Thy pleas-ant pas - tures feed us, For our use Thy folds pre - pare:
Keep Thy flock, from sin de - fend us, Seek us when we go a - stray:
Thou hast mer - cy to re - lieve us, Grace to cleanse, and pow'r to free:
Bless - ed Lord and on - ly Sav - ior, With Thy love our bos - oms fill:

Bless - ed Je - sus, Bless - ed Je - sus, Thou hast bought us, Thine we are;
Bless - ed Je - sus, Bless - ed Je - sus, Hear Thy chil - dren when they pray;
Bless - ed Je - sus, Bless - ed Je - sus, Ear - ly let us turn to Thee;
Bless - ed Je - sus, Bless - ed Je - sus, Thou hast loved us, love us still;

Bless - ed Je - sus, Bless - ed Je - sus, Thou hast bought us, Thine we are.
Bless - ed Je - sus, Bless - ed Je - sus, Hear Thy chil - dren when they pray.
Bless - ed Je - sus, Bless - ed Je - sus, Ear - ly let us turn to Thee.
Bless - ed Je - sus, Bless - ed Je - sus, Thou hast loved us, love us still.

* or A♭6

SHEPHERD OF LOVE

184

Words and Music by
John W. Peterson

Shep - herd of love,_____ You knew I had lost my way; _____
Shep - herd of love,_____ Sav - ior and Lord and Guide, ___

Shep - herd of love, _____ You cared that I'd gone___ a - stray. _____
Shep - herd of love, _____ For - ev - er I'll stay by your

side. _____ You sought and found me, placed a - round me

Strong arms that car - ried me home; _____ No foe can harm me

or a - larm me___ Nev - er a - gain will I roam! _____

185 SOMETHING BEAUTIFUL

Gloria Gaither

William J. Gaither

Some - thing beau-ti-ful, some - thing good;

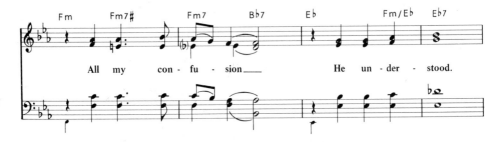

All my con-fu-sion___ He un-der - stood.

All I had to of-fer Him was bro-ken-ness and

strife, But He made some-thing beau-ti-ful of my life.___

SING HALLELUJAH
(TO THE LORD)

186

Based on I Cor. 15:20, Rev.19:1

Linda Stassen

Additional verses

2. Jesus is risen from the dead.
3. Christ is the Lord of Heav'n and earth.
4. Praise be to God forevermore
5. Sing hallelujah to the Lord.

187
Matt. 6:33

SEEK YE FIRST

Karen Lafferty

Descant optional

1. Seek ye __ first the __ King-dom of God, And His __ right-eous - ness.
2. Ask and __ it shall be given un-to you, Seek and ye shall find,
3. Man does not live by bread a __ lone, But by ev - ery word

And all these things shall be ad - ded un-to you! Al - le - lu, al-le - lu - ia!
Knock and the door shall be op-ened un-to you, Al - le - lu, al-le - lu - ia!
That pro __ ceeds from the mouth of the Lord, Al - le - lu, al-le - lu - ia!

Vs. 2 and 3 not part of song as originally written.

SOMETIMES ALLELUIA

188

Words and Music by
Chuck Girard

189

THOU ART HOLY

Ps. 22:3; Rev. 4:11

Gary Johnson

1. Thou art ho - ly, Thou art ho - ly,
2. Thou art wor - thy, Thou art wor - thy
3. Al - le - lu - ia, Al - le - lu - ia,

Dwell - ing in ___ our prais - es, Thou art ho - ly.
To re - ceive ___ our prais - es, Thou art wor - thy.
Al - le - lu ia, Al - le - lu - ia;

THE APOSTLES CREED

190

David Siebels
Arr. by Henry Wiens

SOON AND VERY SOON

191

Words and Music by
Andrae Crouch

192 SOON THE DAY WILL COME

Words and Music by
John Worre

Soon the day will come when ev - 'ry knee shall bow,

Soon the day will come when ev - 'ry tongue shall con - fess _____ Je - sus is

Lord, _____ But I don't want to wait, I want to say it now.

I don't want to wait, so glad - ly I will con - fess: _____ Je - sus is

Lord, _____ Je - sus is Lord.

SPECIAL DELIVERY

193

Easily, with a lilt

Words and Music by
Ron and Carol Harris

1. Nev-er was an-y-one like Him, Nev-er will one be the same; — A ti-ny babe, an in-fant King. We wor-ship and hon-or, the pow'r of His name. O He came
2. Where He went love was there al-so, Where He was love showed the way; — Those who saw knew He was And I see what they saw to this ver-y day. O He came
3. When I'm called I will go glad-ly, I will not grieve for the past; — For I know where I'll be And I will be go-ing to see Him at last. I'm go-ing

Sav-ior ho-ly, go-ing,

SPIRIT OF GOD, DESCEND UPON MY HEART

194

George Croly

Frederick C. Atkinson

1. Spir - it of God, de - scend up - on my heart;
2. Hast Thou not bid us love Thee, God and King?
3. Teach me to feel that Thou art al - ways nigh;
4. Teach me to love Thee as Thine an - gels love,

Wean it from earth through all its puls - es move;
All, all Thine own, soul, heart and strength and mind;
Teach me the strug - gles of the soul to bear,
One ho - ly pas - sion fill - ing all my frame;

Stoop to my weak - ness, might - y as Thou art,
I see Thy cross there teach my heart to cling:
To check the ris - ing doubt, the reb - el sigh;
The bap - tism of the heav'n de - scend - ed Dove,

And make me love Thee as I ought to love.
O let me seek Thee, and O let me find.
Teach me the pa - tience of un - an - swered prayer.
My heart an al - tar; and Thy love the flame. A - men.

195 SPIRIT OF THE LIVING GOD

Words and Music by
Daniel Iverson

SUCH AN OUT OF THE ORDINARY MAN

196

Words and Music by
John Worre
Arr. Henry Wiens

1. Some said He's just a man, an un-us-u-al man, But could He be more, E-ven part of God's plan? He seems dif-f'rent to me, It's not hard to a-gree, He could be the One, the Mes-si-ah to be, when I look in His eyes so sad and so wise, The wrong in my life I can

2. hum-bly to John, tho' He was God's own Son, To be an ex-am-ple to all of His own, said a voice from a-bove "This is my son whom I love," and God's Ho-ly Spir-it came down like a Dove, He was bap-tized that day in the wa-ter that way, But some-thing more hap-pened that

3. taught how to live, that you get what you give, To the lost He had come for to seek and to save, He made blind eyes to see, set the cap-tive ones free, lit-tle chil-dren He said "Let them come un-to me," Such love He would show, and where-ev-er He'd go, From Him liv-ing ri-vers of

SURELY GOODNESS
AND MERCY

197

Based on Psalm 23

Words and Music by
John W. Peterson and
Alfred B. Smith

Sure - ly good - ness and mer - cy shall fol - low—

me all the days, all the days of my life; _____

___ Sure - ly good - ness and mer - cy shall fol - low—

me all the days, all the days of my life. _____

SWEET HOUR OF PRAYER

W. W. Walford

Wm. B. Bradbury

1. Sweet hour of prayer, sweet hour of prayer, That calls me from a world of care,
2. Sweet hour of prayer, sweet hour of prayer, Thy wings shall my pe - ti - tion bear,
3. Sweet hour of prayer, sweet hour of prayer, May I thy con - so - la - tion share,

And bids me at my Fa - ther's throne Make all my wants and wish - es known,
To Him whose truth and faith - ful - ness En - gage the wait - ing soul to bless;
Till, from Mount Pisg - ah's loft - y height, I view my home, and take my flight:

In sea - sons of dis - tress and grief, My soul has oft - en found re - lief,
And since He bids me seek His face, Be - lieve His word and trust His grace,
This robe of flesh I'll drop, and rise To seize the ev - er - last - ing prize;

And oft es - caped the tempter's snare, By thy re - turn, sweet hour of prayer.
I'll cast on Him my ev - 'ry care, And wait, for thee, sweet hour of prayer.
And shout, while pass - ing thro' the air, Fare - well, fare - well, sweet hour of prayer!

199
TAKE MY LIFE,
AND LET IT BE

Frances R. Havergal

C.H.A. Malan

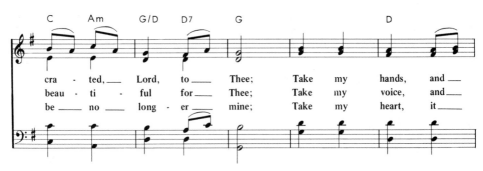

1. Take my life, ___ and ___ let it be Con - se -
2. Take my feet, ___ and ___ let them be Swift and
3. Take my will, ___ and ___ make it Thine, It shall

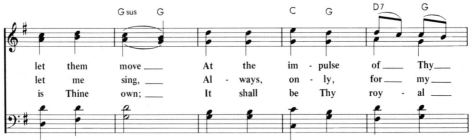

cra - ted, ___ Lord, to ___ Thee; Take my hands, and ___
beau - ti - ful for ___ Thee; Take my voice, and ___
be ___ no ___ long - er ___ mine; Take my heart, it ___

let them move ___ At the im - pulse of ___ Thy ___
let me sing, ___ Al - ways, on - ly, for ___ my ___
is Thine own; ___ It shall be Thy roy - al ___

love, ___ At the im - pulse ___ of Thy love.
King, ___ Al - ways, on - ly, ___ for my King.
throne, ___ It shall be Thy ___ roy - al throne.

TELL THEM

Words and Music by
Andrae Crouch
Arr. Henry Wiens

Tell them ev - en if they don't be-lieve. You just tell them ev-en
Tell them when it seems you are for-sak - en, Just tell them tho' it

if they don't re - ceive, You just tell them for me. Please tell them for me ___ that I
seems your earth is shak - en, Just tell them for me. Please tell them for me ___ that I

love them, ___ And I came to let them know.
love them, ___ And I came to let them know.

Tell that lone-ly man ___ who walks the

cold streets all ___ a-lone. ___ Tell that cry-ing child who has no home.

THE BUILDING BLOCK 201

Words and Music by
Noel Paul Stookey

The Build-ing Block, the build-ing block that was re - ject - ed — be-came the cor - ner - stone — of a whole new world.

1. When I am down, and un-sus- pect - ed — with a bur - den that — does not show. I think what time, has res-ur - rect - ed, and how the sun can make the water flow.

D.C.

2. There is a man, there is a man, who has collected,
   all the sorrows in our eyes.
   He gives us love, as God directed,
   but is seldom recognized.
   CHORUS

3. When all your dreams, when all your dreams,
   have been connected,
   and your vision has been returned.
   Remember, love, you are protected,
   by the truth your heart has learned.
   CHORUS

202

THE CHURCH'S
ONE FOUNDATION

Samuel. J. Stone

Samuel S. Wesley

1. The Church-'s one foun-da-tion, Is Je-sus Christ her Lord;
2. E-lect from ev-'ry na-tion, Yet one o'er all the earth,
3. 'Mid toil and trib-u-la-tion, And tu-mult of her war,
4. Yet she on earth hath un-ion With God the Three in One,

She is His new cre-a-tion By wa-ter and the word:
Her char-ter of sal-va-tion One Lord, one faith one birth;
She waits the con-sum-ma-tion Of peace for-ev-er-more;
And mys-tic sweet com-mun-ion With those whose rest is won:

From Heav'n He came and sought her To be His ho-ly bride; With
One ho-ly name she bless-es, Par-takes one ho-ly food, And
Till, with the vi-sion glo-rious, Her long-ing eyes are blest, And
O hap-py ones and ho-ly! Lord, give us grace that we, Like

His own blood He bought her, And for her life He died.
to one hope she press-es, With ev-'ry grace en-dued.
the great church vic-to-rious Shall be the church at rest.
them, the meek and low-ly, On high may dwell with Thee. A-men.

THE FAMILY OF GOD 203

William J. & Gloria Gaither

William J. Gaither

I'm so glad I'm a part of the fam-'ly of God; I've been washed in the foun-tain,— cleansed by His blood! Joint heirs with Je-sus as we tra-vel this sod, For I'm part of the fam-'ly,— the fam - 'ly of

1. God!_____ I'm so

2. God!_____

Fine

204 THE GREATEST THING

Words and Music by
Mark Pendergrass

THE JOY OF THE LORD

205

A G. V., alt.

Alliene G. Vale

1. The joy____ of the Lord _____ is my strength; The
2. If you____ want ____ joy you must sing for it, If
3. He giv-eth liv-ing wa-ter and I thirst no more, He
4. He heals the bro-ken heart-ed and they cry no more, He

joy____ of the Lord _____ is my strength; The
you____ want ____ joy____ you must shout for it; If
giv-eth liv-ing wa-ter and I thirst no more; He
heals the bro-ken heart-ed and they cry no more; He

joy____ of the Lord _____ is my strength; The
you____ want ____ joy____ you must jump for it; The
giv-eth liv-ing wa-ter and I thirst no more. The
heals the bro-ken heart-ed and they cry no more; The

joy____ of the Lord ____ is my strength.
joy____ of the Lord ____ is my strength.
joy____ of the Lord ____ is my strength.
joy____ of the Lord ____ is my strength.

206 THE KING OF GLORY

Willard F. Jabusch
Based on Ps. 24:7-10; Matt. 4:23-25; 9:33; I Pet. 3:18

Israeli Folk Song

Refrain

The King of glo - ry comes, the na - tion re - joic - es;

O - pen the gates be - fore Him, lift up your voic - es.

Fine

Stanzas

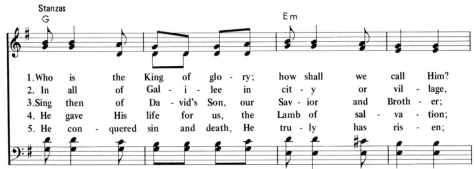

1. Who is the King of glo - ry; how shall we call Him?
2. In all of Gal - i - lee in cit - y or vil - lage,
3. Sing then of Da - vid's Son, our Sav - ior and Broth - er;
4. He gave His life for us, the Lamb of sal - va - tion;
5. He con - quered sin and death, He tru - ly has ris - en;

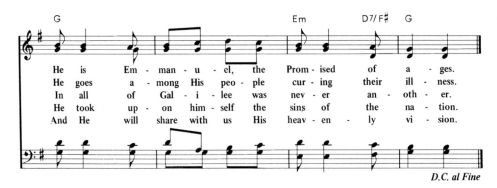

He is Em - man - u - el, the Prom - ised of a - ges.
He goes a - mong His peo - ple cur - ing their ill - ness.
In all of Gal - i - lee was nev - er an - oth - er.
He took up - on him - self the sins of the na - tion.
And He will share with us His heav - en - ly vi - sion.

D.C. al Fine

THE HIDING PLACE

207

Bryan Jeffery Leech

1. In a time of trou - ble _____ in a time for - lorn, _____ There is a hid - ing place _____ where hope is born. In a time of dan - ger _____ when our faith is proved, _____ There is a hid - ing place _____ where we are

2. In a time of sor - row _____ in a time of grief, _____ There is a hid - ing place _____ to give re - lief. In a time of weak - ness, _____ in a time of fear. _____ There is a hid - ing place _____ where God is

THE LAW OF THE LORD   208

Psalm 19:7-11,14

Jo Anne Roberts Graham

1. The law of the Lord is per-fect, con-vert-ing the soul. The tes-ti-mon-y of the Lord is sure, mak-ing wise the sim-ple.

Chorus
More to be de-sired are they than gold, yea, than much fine gold. Sweet-er al-so than hon-ey and the hon-ey - comb.

2. The statutes of the Lord are right,
   rejoicing the heart;
   The commandment of the Lord is pure.
   enlightening the eyes.

   Chorus

3. The fear of the Lord is clean.
   enduring forever;
   The judgements of the Lord are true
   and righteous altogether.

   Chorus

4. Let the words of my mouth, Oh Lord,
   and the meditations of my heart,
   Be acceptable in Thy sight, Oh Lord,
   my strength and my Redeemer.

Last Chorus
Moreover by them is Thy servant warned.
is Thy servant warned.
and in keeping of them there is great
reward.

209   THE LORD BLESS THEE

Chuck Butler

THE LORD BLESS YOU AND KEEP YOU

Farewell Anthem With Sevenfold Amen

210

Words and Music by
Peter C. Lutkn

The Lord bless you and keep you, the Lord lift His coun-te-nance up-

on you; and give you peace, and give you peace, and give you peace, and give you peace, the Lord, the

Lord make His face to shine up-on you, and be and be gracious

and be gra-cious, the Lord be gra-cious, gra-cious un-to

you. A - men, A - men, A - men A - men
A - men, A A - C - men.
you. A - men A - men

211 WE'D LIKE TO THINK

Richard Avery
Donald Marsh

1. We'd like to think the crowd was large, At least five thous-and strong, There pro-ba-bly— were just a few, ____ Who touched by Je - sus; real - ly knew ____ Just who it was who hum - bly rode a - long.
2. We'd like to think that we'd been there To cheer him as he rode, To shout "Hos-an - na!" as he came, ____ To call him by his right - ful name, ____ To pat the donk - ey with its pre-cious load.
3. We'd like to think we'd be a - mong The ones who could fore - see The fright-ful week that lay a - head, ____ Which found our Sav - ior Je - sus dead, ____ And stop the cru - el nail-ing on the tree.
4. We'd like to think we'd stay a - wake And be with him in prayer, De - fend him at __ Geth sem - a - ne, ____ Pro - tect him from the mock - er - y, ____ Re - move the crown of thorns they made him wear.
5. We'd like to think we faith - ful few, We could have changed the past; But God has placed us here and now, ____ A rem - nant band to work out how ____ This time, our time can be re - deemed at last.
6. We'd like to think our crowd is large, But we are still a few. Per - haps our Lord a -gain would choose ____ Just twelve to go with his Good News. ____ So help us, God, with faith to live for you.

THE LORD IS MY LIGHT 212

Ps. 27:1

Music by Paune M. Mills
Arr. by Charles High

life, _____ Of Whom, then, _ Shall I be a - fraid? _____ The Lord is my

D.S. al Fine

213 HALLELUJAH, WHAT A SAVIOUR!

Words and Music by
P. P. Bliss

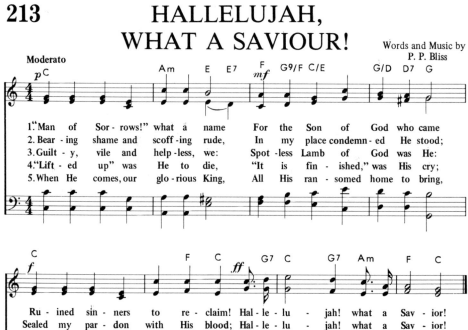

Moderato

1. "Man of Sor - rows!" what a name For the Son of God who came
2. Bear - ing shame and scoff -ing rude, In my place condemn - ed He stood;
3. Guilt - y, vile and help -less, we: Spot -less Lamb of God was He:
4. "Lift - ed up" was He to die, "It is fin - ished," was His cry;
5. When He comes, our glo - rious King, All His ran - somed home to bring,

Ru - ined sin - ners to re - claim! Hal - le - lu - jah! what a Sav - ior!
Sealed my par - don with His blood; Hal - le - lu - jah! what a Sav - ior!
"Full a - tone - ment!" can it be? Hal - le - lu - jah! what a Sav - ior!
Now in heav'n ex - alt - ed high; Hal - le - lu - jah! what a Sav - ior!
Then a - new this song we'll sing; Hal - le - lu - jah! what a Sav - ior!

THERE WERE TWELVE DISCIPLES
(HE HAS CALLED US TOO) 214

Anon.

George A. Minor

There were twelve dis-ci - ples Je - sus called to help him: Si - mon Pe - ter, An - drew,

James, his bro - ther John; Phil - ip, Thom - as, Mat - thew, James, the son of Al - pheus,

Chorus

Thad-deus, Si - mon, Ju - das, And Bar - thol - o - mew. He has called us too,

He has called us too; We are His dis-ci - ples, I am one and you. ples, We his work must do.

215 THE LORD IS MY SHEPHERD

Based on Psalm 23

With assurance

Unknown

The Lord is my__ shep-herd I'll live for Him al-
ways, He leads in green__ pas-tures, I'll live for Him al-
ways. Al-ways, al-ways, I'll live for Him al-ways. Al-

ways. al-ways, I'll live for Him al-ways. The ways.

THE LORD IS PRESENT IN HIS SANCTUARY

216

Words and Music by
Gail Cole

1. The Lord is pres-ent in His sanc-tu-ar - y, let us praise ___ the Lord. The
2. The Lord is pres-ent in His sanc-tu-ar - y, let us delight in the Lord. The
3. The Lord is pres-ent in His sanc-tu-ar - y, let us serve ___ the Lord. The

Lord is pres-ent in His sanc-tu-ar - y, let us praise ___ the Lord.
Lord is pres-ent in His sanc-tu-ar - y, let us delight in the Lord.
Lord is pres-ent in His sanc-tu-ar - y, let us serve ___ the Lord.

Praise Him, praise ___ Him, ___ let us praise ___ the Lord. ___

Praise Him, praise ___ Him, ___ let us praise ___ Je - sus.

217   EVERY EYE SHALL SEE

Words by William J. and Gloria Gaither

Music by William J. Gaither
Arr. by Alex Galvan

Simply-in slow "2"

THE LOVE ROUND

218

Three Part Round

Unknown
Arranged by Charles High

Love, love, love, love, Chris-tians, this is your call; Love your neigh-bor as your-self, for God loves us all. all.

219

THE NEW 23RD

Psalm 23
Adapted by R.C.

Ralph Carmichael

220 THE OLD RUGGED CROSS

Words and Music by
George Bennard

1. On a hill far a-way stood an old rug-ged cross, The em-blem of suf-f'ring and shame; And I love that old cross where the dear-est and best For a world of lost sin-ners was slain.

2. O that old rug-ged cross, so de-spised by the world, Has a won-drous at-trac-tion for me; For the dear Lamb of God left His glo-ry a-bove To bear it to dark Cal-va-ry.

3. In the old rug-ged cross, stained with blood so di-vine, A won-drous beau-ty I see; For 'twas on that old cross Je-sus suf-fered and died To par-don and sanc-ti-fy me.

4. To the old rug-ged cross, I will ev-er be true, Its shame and re-proach glad-ly bear; Then He'll call me some day to my home far a-way, Where His glo-ry for-ev-er I'll share.

Chorus

So I'll cher-ish the old rug-ged cross, the old rug-ged cross, Till my

tro - phies at last I lay down; ____ I will cling to the old rug - ged
cross, the

cross, ____ And ex - change it some day for a crown. ____
old rug - ged cross,

THANK YOU, LORD

221

Words and Music by
Mr. and Mrs. Seth Sykes

G   G7   C   G   G   A7   D7

Thank you, Lord, for sav - ing my soul.   Thank you, Lord, for mak-ing me whole;

G   G7   C   G   G7/B   C   G/D D7 G

Thank you, Lord, for giv - ing to me   Thy great sal - va - tion so rich and free.

THE SOLID ROCK

222

Edward Mote

William B. Bradbury

1. My hope is built on noth-ing less Than Je - sus blood and right-eous-ness;
2. When dark-ness seems to hide His face, I rest on His un - chang-ing grace;
3. His oath, His cov - e - nant, His blood, Sup - port me in the whelm-ing flood;
4. When He shall come with trum-pet sound, Oh, may I then in Him be found;

I dare not trust the sweet-est frame, But whol-ly lean on Je - sus' name.
In ev - ery high and storm-y gale, My an-chor holds with - in the vale.
When all a - round my soul gives way, He then is all my hope and stay.
Dressed in His right-eous - ness a - lone, Fault - less to stand be - fore the throne.

Refrain

On Christ, the sol - id Rock, I stand: All oth - er ground is
sink - ing sand, All oth - er ground is sink - ing sand.

THERE'S A QUIET UNDERSTANDING

223

Words and Music by
Tedd Smith

224 THE WISE MAN AND THE FOOLISH MAN

Matthew 7:24-27

Arr. by Harry Dixon Loes

1. The wise man built his house up-on the rock, The wise man built his
2. The fool-ish man built his house up-on the sand, The fool-ish man built his

house up-on the rock; The wise man built his house up-on the rock,
house up-on the sand; The fool-ish man built his house up-on the sand,

And the rains came tum-bling down. *Chorus* The rains came down and the

floods came up, The rains came down and the floods came up; The

rains came down and the floods came up, And the house on the rock stood fast.
And the house on the sand went smash.

Add this Verse No. 3

So build your Life on the Lord Jesus Christ,
So build your Life on the Lord Jesus Christ,
So build your Life on the Lord Jesus Christ,
And the blessings will come down

Chorus 3 V. only

The blessings come down as the prayers go up,
The blessings come down as the prayers go up,
The blessings come down as the prayers go up,
So build your Life on the Lord.

I LOVE YOU, LORD

225

Words and Music by
Laurie Klein

226 THERE IS A FLAG
(JOY IS THE FLAG)

Words and Music by
Brian Konzelman

There is a flag flown from the cas-tle of my heart, The cas-tle of my heart, the cas-tle of my heart. There is a flag flown from the cas-tle of my heart when the King is in res-i-dence there._____ So raise it high in the sky, let the whole world know, let the whole world know, let the whole world know. So raise it high in the sky, let the

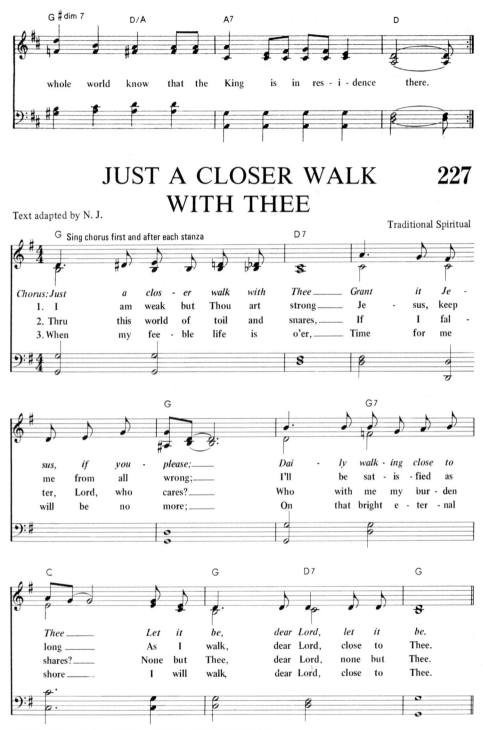

JUST A CLOSER WALK WITH THEE

227

Text adapted by N. J.

Traditional Spiritual

Sing chorus first and after each stanza

Chorus: Just a clos - er walk with Thee_____ Grant it Je -
1. I am weak but Thou art strong_____ Je - sus, keep
2. Thru this world of toil and snares, _____ If I fal -
3. When my fee - ble life is o'er, _____ Time for me

sus, if you - please;_____ Dai - ly walk - ing close to
me from all wrong;_____ I'll be sat - is - fied as
ter, Lord, who cares?_____ Who with me my bur - den
will be no more;_____ On that bright e - ter - nal

Thee_____ Let it be, dear Lord, let it be.
long _____ As I walk, dear Lord, close to Thee.
shares?_____ None but Thee, dear Lord, none but Thee.
shore _____ I will walk, dear Lord, close to Thee.

228 JESUS, WE JUST WANT TO THANK YOU

Words and Music by
William J. Gaither
Arr. by Henry Wiens

HEAR, O LORD, I RAISE MY VOICE

Norman Habel

"Michael"

1. Hear O Lord, I raise my voice, Al - le - lu - ia! You're my help, and I re - joice, Al - le - lu - ia! The Lord's my lamp who lights my way, Al - le - lu - ia. With His help. I can not stray, Al - le - lu - ia!

2. You're my shield, and guard me true Al - le - lu - ia! Lord of Hosts, You keep us now Al - le - lu - ia! Hear O Lord, I raise my voice, Al - le - lu - ia! You're my help. and I re - joice, Al - le - lu - ia!

3. Shouts of glo - ry to the Father Al - le - lu - ia! Shouts of glo - ry to His Son, Al - le - lu - ia! Shouts of glo - ry to the Spirit, Al - le - lu - ia! As it was! and has to be, Al - le - lu - ia!

4. Hear, O Lord, I raise my voice, Alleluia!
   You're my help, and I rejoice, Alleluia.
   The Lord's my lamp who lights my way, Alleluia.
   With His help, I cannot stray, Alleluia!

230 THERE'S NO GREATER NAME

Words and Music by
Michael Baughan

1. There's no great - er name than Je - sus,
   name of him who came to save us,
   In that sav - ing name of Je - sus
   Ev' - ry knee should bow.

2. In our minds by faith pro - fess - ing,
   In our hearts by in - ward bless - ing,
   On our tongues by words con -

231 THEREFORE THE REDEEMED

Isa. 51:11

Ruth Lake

heads. _____ They shall ob - tain glad - ness and

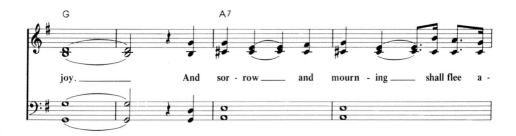

joy. _____ And sor - row ____ and mourn - ing ____ shall flee a -

way. _____ There - fore the re -deemed of the Lord shall re -

turn. re - turn_ and come with sing -ing_____ un - to Zi - on, _____ and ev - er-

last - ing_ joy shall be up - on their heads. _____

232

THEY THAT WAIT
UPON THE LORD

Adapted from Is. 40:31

Stuart Hamblen

THIS IS MY COMMANDMENT **233**

John 15:11-12

Simply

Arr. Betty Pulkingham

This is my command-ment that you love one an-oth-er, that your joy may be full. full: that your joy may be full, that your joy may be full.

Fine

D.C. al Fine

Other verses may be added:

eg. This is my commandment that you 'trust one another. . . '

'serve one another . . .'

'lay down your lives . . . '

234

THIS IS THE DAY

Psalm 118:24

Les Garrett

THIS LITTLE LIGHT OF MINE 235

Arr. by Harry Dixon Loes

236 THOU ART WORTHY

Rev. 4:11

Pauline M. Mills

Thou art wor-thy, Thou art wor-thy, Thou art wor-thy, O Lord, To re-ceive glo-ry, glo-ry and hon-or glo-ry and hon-or and power. For Thou hast cre-a-ted, hast all things cre-a-ted; Thou hast cre-a-ted all things.

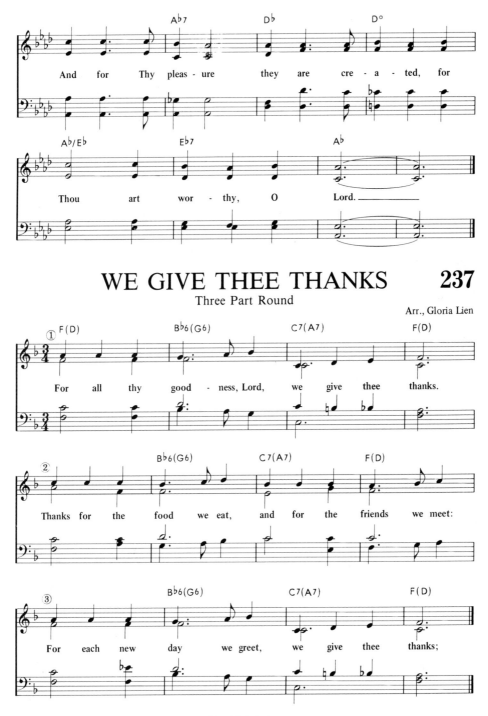

WE GIVE THEE THANKS **237**

Three Part Round

Arr., Gloria Lien

238 THROUGH IT ALL

Words and Music by
Andraé Crouch

1. I've had man-y tears and sor-rows; I've had ques-tions for to-mor-row; there've been times I did'n't know right from wrong;

2. I've been to lots of pla-ces, And I've seen a lot of fa-ces, there've been times I felt so all a-lone;

3. I thank God for the moun-tains, And I thank Him for the val-leys, I thank him for the storms He brought me through

But in ev-'ry sit-u-a-tion God gave bless-ed con-so-la-tion that my

But in my lone-ly ho-urs, yes those pre-cious lone-ly ho-urs, Je-sus

For if I'd nev-er had a prob-lem, I would-n't know that He could solve them, I'd

239 THY LOVING KINDNESS

Adapted from Ps. 63:3-4

Hugh Mitchell

1. Thy lov - ing kind - ness is bet - ter than life. ____
2. I lift my hands, Lord, un - to ____ Thy name. ____

____ Thy lov - ing kind - ness is bet - ter than life.
____ I lift my hands, Lord, un - to Thy name.

My lips shall praise Thee, thus, will I bless Thee ____
My lips shall praise Thee, thus will I bless Thee ____

____ I will lift up my hands un - to Thy Name. ____
____ I will lift up my hands un - to Thy Name. ____

TURN YOUR EYES UPON JESUS 240

Words and Music by
Helen H. Lemmel

Turn your eyes up-on Je - sus, Look

full in His won - der-ful face. _____ And the

things of earth will grow strange - ly dim in the

light of His glo - ry and grace. _____

241 TO GOD BE THE GLORY

Fanny J. Crosby

William H. Doane

1. To God be the glo - ry, great things He hath done, So loved He the world that He gave us His Son. Who yield - ed His life an a - tone - ment for sin, And o - pened the life - gate that all may go in.

2. O per - fect re - demp - tion, the pur - chase of blood, To ev - 'ry be - liev - er the prom - ise of God; The vil - est of - fend - er who tru - ly be - lieves, That mo - ment from Je - sus a par - don re - ceives.

3. Great things He hath taught us, great things He hath done, And great our re - joic - ing thro' Je - sus the Son; But pur - er, and high - er, and great - er will be Our won - der, our trans - port, when Je - sus we see.

242 TWO HANDS

Words and Music by
Tom Coomes & Chuck Butler
Arr. Gloria Lien

1. We're all gath - ered here _____ Be -cause we all be - lieve.
2. Man - y know him well, _____ Oth - ers just by name.

If there's a doubt - er in the crowd, _____ We ask you
If you don't know for what he stands, _____ You've real - ly

not to leave;
much to gain;

Give a lis - ten to his
With _____ faith you can move

sto - ry;
moun - tains;

Hear the mes - sage that we bring.
These are com - mon words but true.

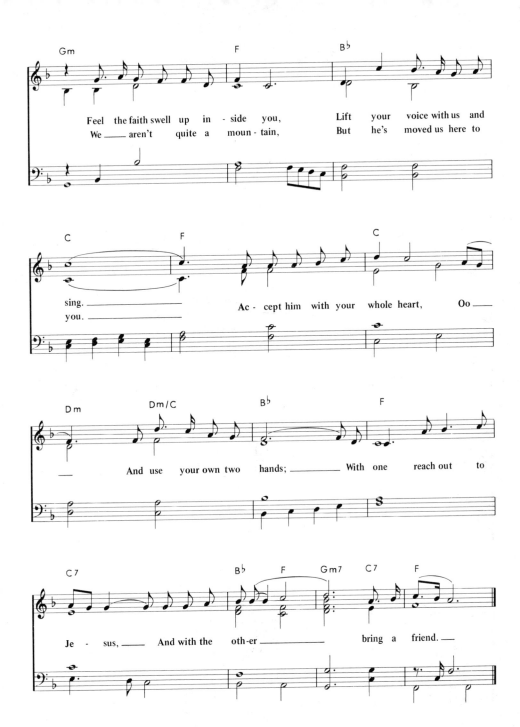

243

UNTO THEE O LORD

Psalm 25: 12,4

Charles Monroe

Un - to thee o Lord do I lift up __ my soul __ un - to thee o Lord

Do I lift up __ my soul _____ o my God __

I trust in thee Let me not be a - shamed.

Let not my en - e - mies triumph __ ov - er me. __

WE ARE FAMILY

2. We are washed, we are sanctified,
   We are cleansed by His blood,
   We are born of the Spirit,
   We are children of the Lord.

3. We are longing for His coming.
   We are looking to the skies,
   We are watching, we are waiting,
   We will fly with Him, we will rise.

4. We will reign with Him forever.
   Men and angels shout and sing,
   All dominion shall be given
   To the family of the King.

245 WE ARE THE CHURCH

Words and Music by
Richard Avery and Donald Marsh

I am the church! You are the church! We are the church to - geth - er! All who fol - low Je - sus All a -round the world! Yes, we're the church to - geth - er!

Fine

1. The church is not a build - ing, The church is not a stee - ple, The
2. We're man - y kinds of peo - ple, With man - y kinds of fac - es, All
3. Some - times the church is march - ing, Some - times it's brave - ly burn - ing, Some -
4. And when the peo - ple gath - er There's sing - ing and there's pray - ing, There's
5. At Pen - te - cost some peo - ple Re - ceived the Ho - ly Spir - it And
6. I count if I am nin - ty Or nine or just a ba - 'by; There's

church is not a rest - ing place, The church is a peo - ple!
col - ors and all a - ges, too, From all times and plac - es.
times it's rid - ing, some - times hid - ing, Al - ways it's learn - ing:
laugh - ing and there's cry - ing some - times, All of it say - ing:
told the Good News thru the world to All who would hear it.
one thing I am sure a - bout and I don't mean may - be;

D.C.

WHAT A FRIEND

Joseph Scriven

Charles C. Converse

246

1. What a Friend we have in Je - sus, All our sins and griefs to bear!
2. Have we tri - als and temp - ta - tions, Is there trou - ble an - y - where?
3. Are we weak and heav - y - la - den, Cum - bered with a load of care?

What a priv - i - lege to car - ry Ev - ery-thing to God in prayer!
We should nev - er be dis - cour - aged, Take it to the Lord in prayer.
Pre - cious Sav - iour, still our ref - uge, Take it to the Lord in prayer.

O what peace we of - ten for - feit, O what need-less pain we bear,
Can we find a friend so faith - ful Who will all our sor - rows share?
Do thy friends de - spise, for - sake thee? Take it to the Lord in prayer;

All be - cause we do not car - ry Ev - ery-thing to God in prayer!
Je - sus knows our ev - ery weak - ness, Take it to the Lord in prayer.
In His arms He'll take and shield thee, Thou wilt find a sol - ace there.

247 WE ARE THE REASON

Words and Music by
David Meece

Slowly, with building intensity

We were the rea - son that He gave His life,__ we were the rea - son that He suf-fered and died.__ To a world that was lost,__ He gave all__ He could give,__ to show us the rea - son to live. live. I've fin 'lly found a rea-son for liv - ing, it's in giv - ing ev-'ry part of my heart.__

248 WE WILL LIFT UP YOUR NAME

Based on Ps. 34:1-3

Glen Aubrey

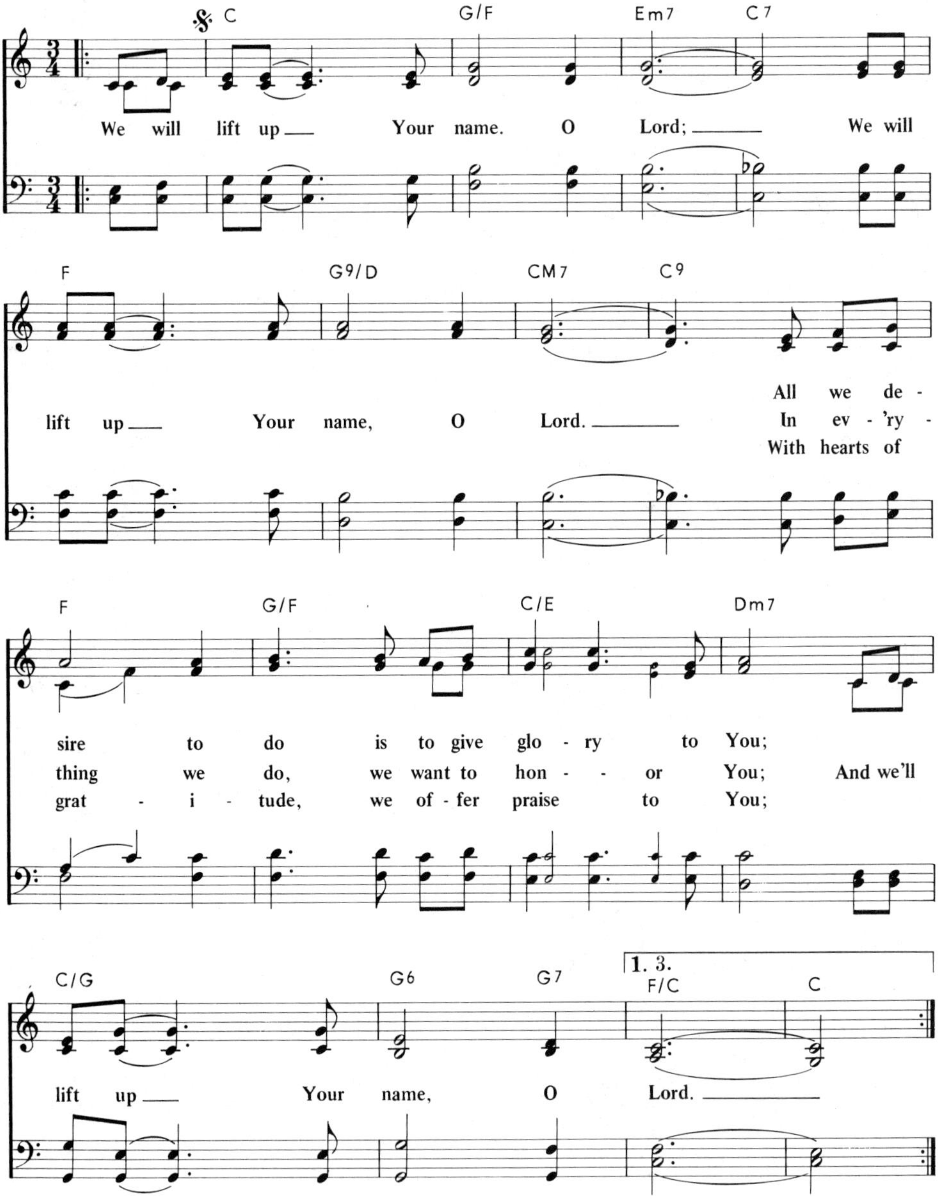
C G/F Em7 C7
We will lift up Your name. O Lord; We will
F G9/D CM7 C9
lift up Your name, O Lord.
All we de - sire to do is to give glo - ry to You;
In ev - 'ry - thing we do, we want to hon - or You; And we'll
With hearts of grat - i - tude, we of - fer praise to You;
F G/F C/E Dm7
C/G G6 G7
lift up Your name, O Lord.
1. 3.
F/C C

2.

Lord. _____ No oth-er name we know that is wor - thy of praise; No oth-er Sav - ior we wor - ship but Je - sus. Lamb of _ God, Prince of Peace, the might - y Con - queror is He; And we'll lift up His _ name for - ev - er. _____ We will

D.S. al Fine

249
WE HAVE COME
INTO HIS HOUSE

Words and Music by
Bruce Ballinger

2. So let's lift up holy hands, and magnify His name, and worship Him . . .
3. So forget about yourself, and concentrate on Him, and worship Him . . .
4. He is all my righteousness, I stand complete in Him, and worship Him . . .

WHEN HE COMETH

250

Rev. W. O. Cushing

Geo. F. Root

1. When He com - eth, when He com - eth To make up His
2. He will gath - er, He will gath - er The gems for His
3. Lit - tle chil - dren, lit - tle chil - dren Who love their Re -

jew - els, All His jew - els, pre - cious jew - els, His loved and His own.
king - dom, All the pure ones, all the bright ones, His loved and His own.
deem - er, Are the jew - els, pre - cious jew - els, His loved and His own.

Chorus

Like the stars of the morn - ing,, His bright crown a - dorn - ing, They shall

shine in their beaut - y, Bright gems for His crown.

251 ZACCHAEUS

Unknown

Music arr. by
Mrs. N. R. SCHAPER

Zac - chae - us was a wee lit - tle man, A wee lit - tle man was

he, He climbed up in a sy - ca - more tree For the Lord he want - ed to

see; And as the Sav - iour passed that way, He looked up in the

tree, Spoken And He said: "Zacchaeus, you come down, For I'm go - ing to your house to -

day, For I'm go - ing to your house to - day."

① Hands in front, right palm raised above left palm. ② Bring palms a little closer. ③ Alternate hands in climbing motion. ④ Shade eyes with right hand and look down. ⑤ Shade eyes with right hands and look up. ⑥ Words are spoken, while looking up and wagging a finger in admonition.
⑦ Clap hands on accented beat.

ZEPHANIAH 3:17

252

Tapu Moala

The Lord thy God in the midst of thee is might-y,

might-y He will save and re-joice over thee with joy, with

joy, He will rest in His love, He will joy o-ver

thee with sing-ing. The Lord thy God in the midst of thee is

might-y, might-y, might-y,

253 WE ARE FREE IN HIM

Source Unknown

way. _____ He is way. _____

WHEN I REMEMBER 254

Source Unknown

Chorus:

No, no, no, no, no, I'll nev-er go back an-y-more, hal-le-lu-ia.

nev-er go back an-y-more.   1. When I re-mem-ber that he died for me, I'll

Verse:

nev-er go back an-y-more, hal-le-lu-ia. nev-er go back an-y-more.

Chorus

2. When I remember that He rose again . . . .
   CHORUS

3. When I remember that He lives in me . . .
   CHORUS

4. When I remember that He's coming soon . . .
   CHORUS

255 WIND, WIND

Jane and Betsy Clowe

Jane Clowe

Wind, wind, blow on me;___ wind, wind, set me free;___

wind, wind, my Fa - ther sent the bless - ed Ho - ly Spi - rit.___

Last time

1. Je - sus told us all a - bout___ you,
2. When we're wea - ry you con - sole___ us;
3. When un - to the Church you came,___ it was
4, Set us free to love our bro - thers;

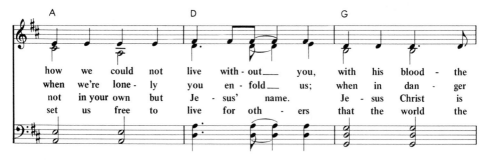

how we could not live with - out___ you, with his blood — the
when we're lone - ly you en - fold us; when in dan - ger
not in your own but Je - sus' name. Je - sus Christ is
set us free to live for oth - ers that the world the

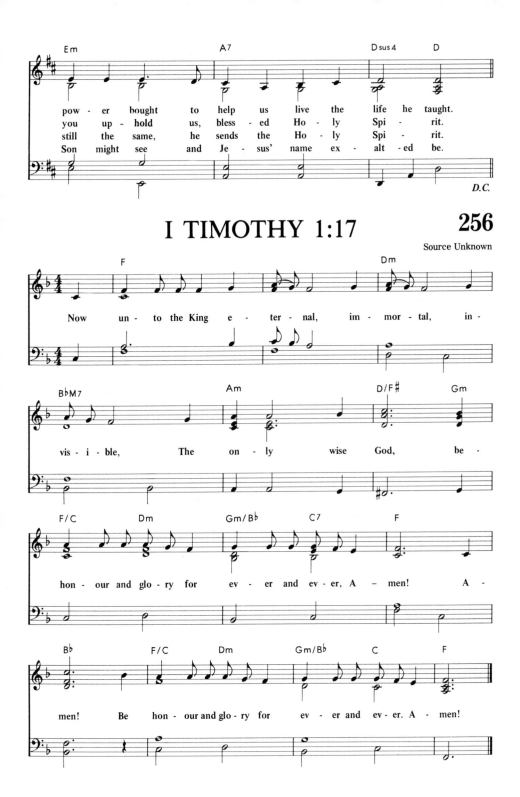

I TIMOTHY 1:17

256

Source Unknown

pow - er bought to help us live the life he taught.
you up - hold us, bless - ed Ho - ly Spi - rit.
still the same, he sends the Ho - ly Spi - rit.
Son might see and Je - sus' name ex - alt - ed be.

D.C.

Now un - to the King e - ter - nal, im - mor - tal, in -

vis - i - ble, The on - ly wise God, be -

hon - our and glo - ry for ev - er and ev - er, A – men! A -

men! Be hon - our and glo - ry for ev - er and ev - er. A – men!

257 WE ARE MADE IN THE IMAGE OF GOD

Words and Music by
Gloria Lien

THANK YOU

258

Walter Van Der Haas
Peter-Paul Van Lelyveld

Martin G. Schneider

1. Thank You for giv-ing me the morn-ing, Thank You for ev-'ry day that's new, Thank You that I can know my wor-ries Can be cast on You. —

2. Thank You for all my friends and broth-ers, Thank You for all the men that live, Thank You for e-ven great-est en-e-mies I can for-give. —

3. Thank You I have my oc-cu-pa-tion, Thank You for ev-'ry pleas-ure small, Thank You for mu-sic, light and glad-ness, Thank You for them all. —

* After stanza three, the key of each succeeding stanza may rise one-half step, if so desired.

4. Thank You for many little sorrows,
Thank You for ev'ry kindly word,
Thank You that ev'rywhere Your guidance
Reaches ev'rywhere

5. Thank You _ I see Your Word has meaning,
Thank You _ I know Your Spirit here,
Thank You because You love all People,
Those both far and near.

6. Thank You, O Lord _ You spoke unto us,
Thank You, that for our words you care,
Thank You, O Lord _ You came among us,
Bread and wine to share.

7. Thank You, O Lord _ Your love is boundless,
Thank You that I am full of You,
Thank You, _ You make me feel so glad
And thankful as I do.

259 SING UNTO GOD

Psalm 68:4

Sing un-to God, sing praises to His name. Sing un-to God, sing praise to His name. Ex-tol Him that rideth on the heavens by His name, ex-tol Him that rideth on the heavens by His name, Ex-tol Him that rideth on the heavens by His name, by His name, JAH. And re-joice be-fore Him and re-joice be-fore Him, and re-joice, re-joice be-

fore Him And re - fore _____ Him!

THE BOND OF LOVE 260

John 17:23; Eph. 4:1-3; Col. 2:2

Words and Music by
Otis Skillings

1. We are one in the bond of love; We are
2. Let us sing now,_____ ev - 'ry, one; Let us

one in the bond of love. _____ We have joined our spir - it with the
feel His _____ love be - gun. _____ Let us join our hands,_ that the

Spir - it of God; We are one in the bond of love.
world will_____ know We are one in the bond of love.

261 IN THE GARDEN

Words and Music by
C. Austin Miles

1. I come to the gar-den a-lone___ While the dew is still on the
2. He speaks, and the sound of His voice___ Is so sweet the birds hush their
3. I'd stay in the gar-den with Him___ Though the night a-round me be

ros - es; And the voice I hear fall-ing on my ear The Son of God dis-
sing - ing; And the me-lo-dy that He gave to me With-in my heart is
fall - ing; But He bids me go thru the voice of woe, His voice to me is

clos - es.
ring - ing.   And He walks with me and He talks with me, And He
call - ing.

tells me I am His own.___ And the joy we share as we

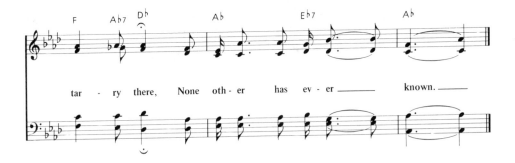

tar - ry there, None oth - er has ev - er _____ known. _____

O COME, LET US ADORE HIM 262

Adapted

From Canrus Diversi

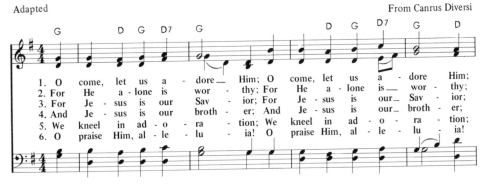

1. O come, let us a - dore ___ Him; O come, let us a - dore Him;
2. For He a - lone is wor - thy; For He a - lone is ___ wor - thy;
3. For Je - sus is our Sav - ior; For Je - sus is our ___ Sav - ior;
4. And Je - sus is our broth - er; And Je - sus is our ___ broth - er;
5. We kneel in ad - o - ra - tion; We kneel in ad - o - ra - tion;
6. O praise Him, al - le - lu - ia! O praise Him, al - le - lu - ia!

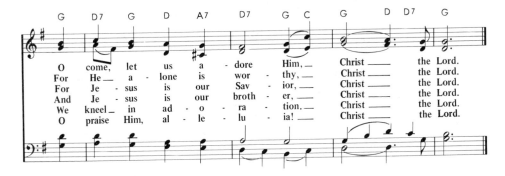

O come, let us a - dore Him, ___ Christ _____ the Lord.
For He ___ a - lone is wor - thy, ___ Christ _____ the Lord.
For Je - sus is our Sav - ior, ___ Christ _____ the Lord.
And Je - sus is our broth - er, ___ Christ _____ the Lord.
We kneel ___ in ad - o - ra - tion. ___ Christ _____ the Lord.
O praise Him, al - le - lu - ia! ___ Christ _____ the Lord.

263

NOW THANK
WE ALL OUR GOD

Martin Rinkart
Tr. Catherine Winkworth

Johann Cruger

DOXOLOGY

264

Thomas Ken

Jimmy Owens

Praise God ____ from ____ whom all bless - ings

flow. Praise Him, ____ all crea - tures here ____ be -

low. Praise Him ____ a - bove, ye heav - en - ly

host. Praise Fa - ther, Son, and Ho - ly Ghost.

WORSHIP ORDER NO. 1

Prelude
Opening Hymn
The Welcome
Announcements
Congregational Hymn

WE CONFESS OUR SIN

Lord, have mercy on us. In this hour, help us see our sin and desire a fresh start with You. Help us see the shortcomings in our lives and look to You for answers to our problems. Give us a new vision of what life can be like. Teach us to hope, to love, to give, and to have faith. Lord, have mercy on us.

WE HEAR THE GOOD NEWS

Our God has heard the cries of His people and has had mercy on us. He has seen our need and provided for our salvation. He has seen our condition and provided the solution. He has seen our hearts and given us a Savior. Through the death and resurrection of Jesus Christ, our sin is no longer a weight that holds us down. We are free to live in victory, free from the sin of our self-deceit and free from Satan's power. Praise God for His goodness.
Hymn of Praise
Scripture Readings for the Day

AFFIRMATION OF FAITH

We believe in God — the Creator of all things — the source of all goodness and love. He is our God and we are His people.

We believe in Jesus Christ — the Son of God — true God yet true man. He was crucified, died, and was buried for our sin — that we might be free and know the joy of life. He was raised on the third day and ascended to heaven. He will come again in power and glory to judge both the living and the dead.

We believe in the Holy Spirit — the power of God at work inside of us.

We believe in the church of God — His people of faith throughout the world.

We believe that our sin is forgiven and that we will live together with God for now and throughout eternity.   Amen

THE MESSAGE FROM THE WORD

Offering
SPECIAL MUSIC
A Time for Prayer (you are invited to come to the altar to pray)
Benediction
Closing Hymn
Postlude

WORSHIP ORDER NO. 2
A CELEBRATION OF FAITH

Prelude
Opening Hymn
Opening Prayer
Welcome to Worship
Distribution of Welcome Folders
Announcements
A Hymn of Faith

CONFESSION

Lord, we confess our lack of faith. We see a glimpse of what we ought to be and we know we fall short of the goal. We desire faith that is solid and unchanging, yet we crumble under trials and temptations. We want to be strong, but we know our weakness. Our sinful condition strips us of any spiritual gain that we humanly devise. Lord, forgive us. Accept us as we are, unworthy for the task, yet gifted for Your purposes. Grant us Your gift of Faith.

ABSOLUTION

Our God is a great God. He knows our needs for all areas of life. He knows our weakness and our unbelieving hearts. Yet, He loved us enough to die on a cross to provide forgiveness of our sin. Now the focus is not on the faith that we can muster, but on the great gifts He gives daily as we trust Him. God has given us the gift of faith — faith for the moment...faith for every trial...faith for every temptation...faith for every difficult situation. Praise God for His gift of faith.

Hymn of Praise
Scripture Lessons for the Day

AFFIRMATION OF FAITH

I have faith in God — because of His great love for me.
I believe that He created me and all that I have. All things belong to
  Him.
I have faith in Jesus — because of His great love for me.
I believe that He died on a cross for my sin — conquered death and the
  power of evil — and was raised to life on the third day. His death is mine—
  His resurrection is mine — New life is mine
  because of His words and work.
I have faith in the Holy Spirit — because of His great love for me.
I believe that the Holy Spirit is present here among us — and lives
  within each child of God. He continues to call people to Himself, and to
  build up the church of Christ. Through Him I have power to stand in
  strength against all adversity.
I believe that Jesus is coming again to unite all believers for all eternity.
  Amen.

Offering
Special Music
Sermon
Prayers (you are invited to the altar to pray)
Benediction
Closing Hymn
Postlude

© 1984 Handt Hanson

WORSHIP ORDER NO. 3
A CELEBRATION OF DAILY BREAD
(Communion)

Prelude
Opening Hymn
Opening Prayer
Welcome to Worship
Distribution of Welcome Pads
Announcements
Hymn

WE CONFESS OUR SIN (together)

Lord, we confess our sin. You have promised to provide all of our needs, and yet we mistrust your promise. We know the futility of our own ambitions and our inability to do that which we desire. Today we recognize the sin within us, and ask that You forgive us. Lord, in Your mercy, give us daily bread, not only for our bodies — but as food for our spirits. Forgive our sin and cleanse us so that we are pleasing in Your sight and minister in Your service.

WE HEAR THE GOOD NEWS

Our God is a great God. He provides for all our needs. He gives us daily bread and meets every spiritual need. Our sin no longer controls us. Our response to His love is the focus for our lives. The death of His Son, Jesus Christ, has paid the cost of our sin and has set us free to live in victory. We are forgiven. We are sons and daughters of the King. We are ministers to each other. Praise God for His daily provision for our every need.

Hymn of Praise
Scripture Readings for the Day
AFFIRMATION OF FAITH

I believe in God who created all things and continues to create new life within us.

I believe in Jesus — Son of God — Son of man — The Savior of the World. By His life, His death, and His resurrection I can know the true depth of human possibility and experience the true joy of meaningful life.

I believe that the Holy Spirit is present — now and always — calling us to faith, giving us His gifts and empowering us for service.

I believe that the community of believers called the church can experience the fullness of life through the Word, the sacraments and all that we do. Amen.

Sermon
Offering (all the gifts, including the elements, are brought to the altar)
Special Music
COMMUNION LITURGY
The Invitation

Leader: Welcome to the celebration! God who supplies our every need has given us this meal to share.

People: Lord, we thank You for the bread of eternal life.

Leader: We come to the table, acknowledging our shortcomings and our need to experience His presence in bread and wine.

People: Lord, we thank You for the bread of eternal life.

The Words of Institution For the Bread   Matthew 26:26,27
The Words of Institution For the Wine   Matthew 26:28,29
The Lord's Prayer
The Distribution
Distribution Hymns (sung together during the distribution)
The Blessing
The Benediction
Closing Hymn
Postlude

WORSHIP ORDER NO. 4

Prelude
Opening Hymn
Opening Prayer
Welcome to Worship
Distribution of Welcome Folders
Congregational Hymn

CONFESSION

Lord, God of our tomorrows, we confess our sinful condition before You. We desire something better than what we have and what we are. We know ourselves too well and see our human frailty. We know that our temporary gods are vulnerable and will crumble under the test. We realize that our desires are fickle and backfire on us at the worst times. God of our tomorrows, give us Your forgiveness. Let us see today the promise of something better in our lives.

ABSOLUTION

Our God is a tomorrow God. He knows our past and He knows where we are headed. He knows our needs and desires His children to come to Him in prayer. As we confess our sin to Him, He is faithful and will forgive our sin and set us right with Himself. He knows that **He is** what we desire and that true fulfillment comes in knowing Him. His promise of something better is found in His forgiveness and in His love. Praise God for His goodness.

Hymn of Praise
Scripture Lessons for the Day

AFFIRMATION OF FAITH

Apostles Creed
Offering
Special Music
Sermon
Prayers (you are invited to the altar to pray)
Hymn for Prayer
Benediction

Leader: Go in peace. You are the forgiven people of God.
People: We will celebrate forgiveness in every tomorrow. We will celebrate forgiveness in the week ahead through acts of kindness, times of listening concern, and deeds of generosity.
Leader: Go in peace. You are the forgiven people of God.
People: We have heard the good news. We will share the good news.
Leader: The Lord be with you. Go and serve in His name.   Amen.

Closing Hymn
Postlude

WORSHIP ORDER NO. 5
A COMMUNION CELEBRATION

Prelude
Opening Hymn
Opening Prayer
Welcome to Worship
Distribution of Welcome Pads
Announcements
Hymn

WE CONFESS OUR SIN (together)

Lord, we come before You in prayer today, asking for forgiveness. We have not loved as we ought to love, we have not given as we ought to give, and we have fallen short of the mark of truly being your obedient sons and daughters. We recognize our sin and in this moment of silence, we privately remember our shortcomings in love and life. (silence for reflection)

WE HEAR THE GOOD NEWS

God, our heavenly Father, hears the prayers of His children and answers those prayers. Our prayer for forgiveness is answered in the person of Jesus Christ, His Son, who died for our sin that we might have new life in Him. The distance between God and ourselves has been brought together by His love made perfect in the sacrifice of His Son. To those who believe His word of truth He gives the power to be the people of God. Praise God for His gift of love to us.

Hymn of Praise

Scripture Readings for the Day
Affirmation of Faith
    The Nicene Creed
Pastoral Prayers
Sermon
Offering (the elements and the tithes and offerings are brought to the altar)
Special Music

THE COMMUNION

Leader: We declare ourselves to be Easter people.
People: We have come to share in the table that He has prepared for us.
Leader: He took the bad news of sin and guilt and changed it to Good News through His dying and rising for us.
People: We are here to celebrate that Good News and the presence of Christ with us.
Leader: And He took the bread, blessed it, and broke it. He said to His disciples —
People: "Take, eat; this is my body."
Leader: Also, He took a cup of wine. After saying thanks, He gave it to them saying —
People: "Drink of it, all of you, for this is my blood of the covenant. It is poured out for the forgiveness of sins. Do this to remember me."
Leader: We thank You, Lord God, for these elements given in love for us. Accept us, forgive us, and heal us — that we might live lives that are pleasing to you.
The Lord's Prayer
The Distribution
Distribution Hymns (sung by the congregation during the distribution)
The Blessing
The Benediction
Closing Hymn
Postlude

TOPICAL INDEX

Compiled by Rev. Mark T.
Hannemann, Dale Pust,
and Dave Anderson

SCRIPTURAL INDEX

compiled by Rev. Mark T. Hannemann

INDEX

*Indicates page number in first edition.

*Indicates page number in first edition.

195
243
225
234
60

GGAG CDE
GGGG AG~~CE~~ ~~BA~~ ΣΔ
Ε GGGGG A GG

F G C